FINCHINGFIELD TALES

Finchingfield Tales

A book of country gossip
in bygone years

Dixon Smith

Illustrations by Ken Thomas

IAN HENRY PUBLICATIONS

First published by Denham House in 1983
This edition 1993

© copyright, Dixon Smith, 1983

ISBN 0 86025 507 7

Printed by
Loader Jackson Printers
Unit C, Old Oak Close, Arlesey, Bedfordshire SG15 6XD
for
Ian Henry Publications, Ltd.
20 Park Drive, Romford, Essex RM1 4LH

FOREWORD

Not so very long ago there were no motor cars, no radio, no television, no pops and no cinema. Farmhouses were dimly lit in winter evenings by paraffin lamps and candles. You might wonder how country folk amused themselves in those days. The men, mostly dedicated to their work, their wives, their large families, were tied to their homes. Working hours were almost incessant but the sabbath was kept holy. On that day no avoidable labour was permitted, though friends and neighbours could always be visited. In winter an evening journey in some form of horse-drawn vehicle, always a small adventure, would tend to take place when the moon was full. After arrival and stabling the horse, the visitor could depend on the excellence of the food, drink, and that everlasting form of entertainment, 'gossip'. In those days - work, food and gossip made up most of the life of the country folk, and there were some who excelled in them all.

For centuries the clearing house of all the gossip of the countryside villages, such as Finchingfield, was the weekly market. The market at Braintree, an Essex town forty miles north of London, was established by Royal Charter in 1195. The Charter was purchased by the Bishop of London, who not only owned most of the parish, but also had his palace on Chapel Hill. For centuries the market gave a permanent economic basis to the town by providing an outlet for country produce and services to rural industry. In 1839 the Corn Exchange was built and, by 1860, trade had expanded to 8,000 bushels of wheat, barley, and oats each week, as well as beans, peas and oil seeds grown in the area. Trade was helped enormously in 1848 by the construction of the railway 'costing £40,000 per mile', which not only brought cheap transport to the district and enabled crops and livestock to be taken to London, but also brought cheap imported cattle food for the livestock fatteners in the district. This food included rice meal, Indian peas, maize and the residue of the oil extraction industry in the form of linseed and cotton seed cake.

On Wednesdays the Corn Exchange would be crowded with

local farmers bringing samples of their corn to trade with the millers and merchants who rented stands or desks in the hall. Here, also, were to be found the hay and straw buyers catering for the thousands of horses which provided London's haulage and transport. Threshing machine contractors, who owned and organized the dozen or so threshing tackles which operated in the district, would attend. The implement agents, as they were called, would take orders for ploughshares and spare parts for the primitive farm equipment then in use.

The cattle market centred round the livestock auction, trade was largely influenced by dealers' 'rings'. There was also a market for private bargaining of livestock on the site of the present Town Hall.

It will be seen that the main revenue of the surrounding countryside passed through Braintree, some of which would be spent by the weekly visitors. How was the town equipped to cater for them? In 1860 it had 2 brewers, 5 malsters and 31 inns, 6 millers, 5 saddlers or harness makers, a coachbuilder, a coachsmith and spring maker, 5 wheelwrights, a millwright, 10 blacksmiths, 4 whitesmiths (tinsmiths), together with lawyers, doctors and a vet. The fair sex were catered for by milliners, dressmakers and most important, the Braintree staymaker.

It was often said farmers made the weekly market a day's holiday from the farm and the main business in the Corn Exchange was the exchange of 'Gossip'. Indeed market day was the time for the farmer to dress in his best breeches, boots and buskins and, in his smart pony and trap with gleaming harness, with his wife in her best bonnet and ribbons drive to this important centre of their world.

Prices were constantly fluctuating, an aspect of business upon which it was vitally important for the farmer to be informed. At market he would learn who was a likely buyer for any farm commodity, who would pay the best price, and, most essential, who was likely to be a bad payer.

In country villages the then all prevailing religious observance formed the backbone of a sense of Parish friendship and neighbourliness. The constant effort to 'make ends meet' became a bond of mutual helpfulness difficult to imagine today.

I

OLD THOMAS, 1886

Old Thomas Smith, the miller, climbed into his dogcart and set off from his home near Finchingfield to Braintree market. Week in, week out, on market day, he made the 10 mile journey from his two mills, the riverside watermill and the windmill. The journey took an hour and a half; Polly, his cob, was always getting tired when going up the long hill into the town. Old Thomas enjoyed these weekly excursions. He observed with close attention the crops growing in fields adjacent to the road, all the land owned by large estates, and let to tenants of an infinite variety of personality and competence. Thomas divided the tenant farmers into two classes, 'cap-touchers' and 'thrusters'. Bad or impecunious landlords tended to have bad land agents, which meant poor tenants. The landlords had to be content with low rents and plenty of cap-touching. It needed a good or wealthy landlord to put up with a thruster, who might be liable to overbid him in an auction sale or over-ride him to the hounds.

All the farmers in the Finchingfield district were Thomas' customers. After harvest, in the autumn when the threshing tackles had worked their stacks, the farmers brought samples of their threshed corn to the Corn Exchange to bargain and sell. Thomas did a busy trade in grinding their home grown corn, he bought their wheat, and, indeed, many of his smaller customers relied on their wheat sale to settle their feedstuff and grinding accounts. From Old Thomas they bought wheat offal, a by-product of the flour business, sometimes mixed with ground barley and beans to fatten their pigs, sheep and bullocks.

Thomas did a thriving trade. Forty years of honest dealing and reliable service now kept both his mills grinding to full capacity. When there was plenty of rushing water or a good wind, his mills worked round the clock. He had two sons: Samuel, the eldest, looked after the watermill. At weekends he wound down the flood gates at twelve o'clock on Saturday night, pulling hem up again and re-starting the mill at 12.05 a.m. on Monday morning, thus observing the twenty-four hours of the

Sabbath. Old Thomas' younger son, Frank, a strapping 17 year old, took care of the windmill. The work was intermittent. Corn form the top of the mill was fed into the mill-stones and descended into a bin as meal. The meal bin must be periodically emptied into sakes. Young Frank read Shakespeare by the light of a candle lantern in between emptyings He acquired a disconcerting habit of producing an apt quotation on any subject that attracted his notice.

Frank had a pronounced tendency to avoid working in the mills or with his self-confident and much older brother. He would work the windmill in the daytime only if there was no other work on Old Thomas' small farm, or if the mill-stones required 'dressing'. The constant grinding wore down the face of the stones, which then had to be 'dressed' with a 'mill bill', a heavy wooden shaft with a cold chisel fixed in its head. With this implement, radiating furrows were chipped into the face of the mill stone. From these furrows secondary grooves were chipped at a tangent and parallel to each other. Frank would chip the furrows just a little too deep, so an occasional whole grain would find its way into the meal. These deep furrows ensured a maximum output of grist.

Old Thomas' wife, who baked bread weekly to keep the miller in touch with the quality of his flour, was continually reminding him he would have to do something about his youngest son. Do something: but what? The miller driving his pony and trap through the countryside to maker reflected on the sequence of events which had brought him to his present state.

When Old Thomas was a boy, his father, the hot-tempered Benjamin Smith, farmed Claypit Hall, the family farm, which, though somewhat small, was extremely fertile. In addition to this enterprise, Benjamin had also managed a large farm for a bachelor uncle, who had inherited most of the family fortune. One day, about 50 years ago, hopes of inheriting the estate were dashed when the uncle and Benjamin were inspecting a distant field. The horsemen were unhooking their horses at the end of the day's stint. Benjamin and his uncle borrowed one of the horses to give them a lift back to the farmstead. Travelling pillion, Benjamin addressed an important question about the next day's work. The uncle was deaf and like other deaf people, prone to not listening. There was no response and the query was repeated, still with no answer. Alas, Benjamin's hot temper flashed.

"Damn the deaf old fool," he expostulated, "Might as well address a gate post. It would at least have as much sense as he had in his head. They are both made of wood!"

The uncle heard all this. On reaching the farm there was a swearing match. They parted never to meet again. The uncle told his house-keeper that Benjamin Smith might be Benjamin Smith, but he would never have any of his money. Nor did he, for soon after, Benjamin died of blood poisoning.

This left Old Thomas' mother with a growing family to bring up on just the small family farm, which, when her husband died, was managed by a cattle dealing executor of doubtful honesty named Jimmy Gatward. He managed the farm as he did everything else, to his own advantage.

Because the family funds were somewhat curtailed, Old Thomas had been apprenticed to Andrew Letch, the miller who lived in the adjacent parish. At length, Old Thomas had succeeded him. He soon built up a thriving business with the aid of an enormously strong mill hand. Old Thomas recalled the time when he once accepted a wager with this mill hand for half a sovereign as to who could carry the most weight. Thomas tied two sacks of beans together, each weighing 19 stones, 532 pounds, and carried them round the windmill 'roundhouse'. The mill hand then tied two sacks of flour together each weighing 20 stones, 560 pounds, and carried them round. Old Thomas had had to pay up.

Claypit Hall was farmed by Thomas' elder brother, Mathew, a man who knew everyone's business except his own. The fertile farm, every acre of which was visible from the top of the windmill, became choked with weeds and produced exceedingly poor crops. Time went by and now young Frank, who had an instinct for the land, was never tired of complaining of the bad husbandry of his relation.

As Polly trotted quietly along the dusty road, these ruminations returned Old Thomas' latest worry to his thoughts.

However hard he tried to run his family and his business, something always turned up to put sand in the gears.

A couple of weeks ago it had become apparent that a pair of otters had dug a tunnel and a den under the sluice from the head-water of the mill into the soak dyke. The dyke and sluice were provided so the head water could be drawn past the mill in times of emergency. The entrance to the otter's den was under water, and the den itself was under the side of a wooden bridge over the soak dyke, so giving the vermin a dry warm bed. The entrance tunnel had caused a leak from the head water to the soak dyke. It was only a question of time before the leak developed into a rush of water and there would be no power for the mill.

Old Thomas had a favourite motto, 'never worry about the water when it has once passed the mill'. But water before the mill was another matter. He told Frank to get up early and shoot the otters. Did they not live on fish, and was not Frank a keen angler? Thomas was surprised to meet with evasion, if not actual refusal; but his remark that perhaps he could get his nephew Martin to shoot the vermin, produced a thunderous scowl on his son's face, far more expressive than words. Martin was a very good shot and boasted of the foxes he had bagged. He was good at all sports, drank heavily, and was useless on his father's farm.

The otter's den would have to be dug out and the bank packed with clay. Thomas, as was the custom, would have to ask permission from Mathew to dig a load. He did not like to ask a favour of his brother, who owed him a lot of money. Last week when travelling to market he had been considering how best to tackle this urgent problem. He had returned to ind it solved. Frank had taken 'French' leave, dug and carted a load of clay from Claypit Hall, let the water down, dug out the otter's den, packed the bank with clay and filled the den with sacking soaked in tar. He had done a good job, but contemptuously ignored his uncle.

For mile after mile, Polly trotted rhythmically, pulling her master to market. It gave Old Thomas time to think.

It was clear, thought Old Thomas, that his sons were beyond

6

his control. Samuel was virtually running the milling business and running it very well. Instead of flour ground from home grown wheat, carefully selected, carefully bought, carefully mixed and carefully ground, he plunged heavily into Manitoba wheat, imported from Canada. It made whiter flour and whiter bread, and it was now being claimed it made more loaves per sack of flour. The sea-port millers with their roller mills and Manitoba wheat were monopolising all the city flour trade which could be reached by rail or sea, though they required large bulk orders to make their business economic and could not compete with Old Thomas' widespread trade to village bakers.

Old Thomas had reminded Samuel their trade had hitherto be two way. They had sold their crushed oats and pig meal to farmers to feed their stock, and bought their wheat, often to settle their milling account. "Use Manitoba wheat and you will sell more flour and still buy the same amount of home grown wheat to mix with it," his son had replied, "you can sell all the wheat offal you can make, from grinding more flour, and sell it for more per ton than you pay for the wheat. You will have to be sharper on farmers who can't or won't pay. I have no fancy for working hard to lose money. We can get all The trade we want without dud customers."

Old Thomas thought about the severe lesson with bad debts. Many years ago when times were very hard in the countryside, some of the village bakers had been silly enough to let the farmworkers run into debt with their bread. There was no money about, a man with a large family earning twelve shillings a week could only 'pay as he went' or not at all. The farmworkers had not paid the bakers, the bakers had not paid the miller. Old Thomas had been sorry for them and not pressed too hard. When the bakers could not pay the miller, they bought flour from a merchant. When they did not pay the merchant, they were bankrupted. Old Thomas received 'less in the pound' than if his heart had been harder in the beginning.

Now Samuel was suggesting they equip themselves with a set of roller mills, powered by one of those new oil engines.

They cost the earth and Old Thomas was doubtful if the bank would let them have enough money. His son had no such doubts. "We shall make better flour and sell more of it. We shall make more offal to sell for pig food. Farmers who keep pigs turn their money over quicker. When they sell their pigs they'll be able to pay our bills," Samuel had told his father.

"But what can I do about Frank?" mused Old Thomas, as the journey to Braintree market clip-clopped gently along the narrow country road.

Frank was possessed of huge strength and restless energy. He loathed the domineering and natural leadership of a brother 10 years older than himself. He loved working on the small arm attached to the mill. Here he kept his own pigs, was paid no wages, but in return he never paid anything for his pig food which came from the mill in increasing quantities. He was mad about horses, had taken a young farm-horse and broken it in for cart work, and lately taken a wild thoroughbred colt to break for the Master of Staghounds. "Most likely break his neck," Old Thomas had said to his wife. Still, breaking the colt in 1886 had brought the custom of the hunt stable to the mill. Old Thomas hoped the Master of Staghounds was as rich as he was reputed and would pay his accounts with respectable promptitude.

It was a fine October day. August had been wet for harvest, but September had belatedly lived up to its reputation, 'there are always twenty-one fine days in September'. The farmers had at last cleared their fields of the sodden sheaves of corn and were proceeding with cultivations for the next crop. As Old Thomas' pony and trap passed the farms, he noticed Seabrook was mucking his stubbles, Young Bradridge had three teams ploughing in one field, all working on one setch, one plough was mounted with a bean barrow. "So Bradridge was sowing twenty acres with beans. It was a nice piece of tender clay land and very clean, it should grow a good crop, come to that, twenty-acre always did." Thomas could never remember a bad crop on that field during all the years he had been driving to market.

Further along, a flock of gulls were busy where the thousand acre farmer, Joseph Smith, had four teams working m one field.

As Old Thomas passed, he was made aware by his nose, as well as his eyes, of the attraction for the gulls. Joseph Smith was in fact ploughing in herrings. The herring boats had been landing enormous catches at Yarmouth. What could not be salted into barrels were loaded into railway trucks and sent to Rayne Station from whence Joe carted them. It was a good thing he had plenty of horse power or the gulls would consume the stinking fish faster than they could be ploughed in. Thomas recalled how Quaker Joe had told him of another Quaker, William Penn, the early coloniser in America. He was friendly to the Indians who had shown him how to make maize grow by planting a seed on top of a buried fish. Joseph Smith had always been a good friend of Old Thomas whose family had also sprung from Quaker stock.

At last the long hill into Braintree lay ahead, Polly slowed to walking pace, Old Thomas got out of the trap to lead her. He 'put up' at Turner's stables where both man and horse could be sure of wholesome food at a wholesome charge. The 'flash set' put up at the White Hart, which provided a lavish 'ordinary' on market days. There they could sit down to cards and drink for as long as they wished. It was said Nick Oakes and Hicks Goodchild had been known to come to market on Wednesday and stop at the White Hart playing cards and drinking till it was time to go and pay the men on their farms on Friday.

***

On the Corn Exchange Old Thomas had a stand or desk just opposite the entrance. He had long shared this with Reuben Hunt, a resourceful and enterprising individual who had started a small iron foundry in the rural district to make some of the primitive farm machinery then in use. It may have been the commanding position of the stand which persuaded the iron founder to share it with a miller. On the other hand, Reuben's frugality was notorious. He was known to share a daily newspaper with Tom Mann who had a sawmill across the road from Reuben's 'counting house'. Whether it was due to frugality or a flair to advertise himself and his products in prominent positions, the foundry prospered. Reuben obtained a contract to supply axle boxes for railway rolling stock and other industrial work. This enabled him to endow a grammar school. Three generations later saw one of his descendants at the head of the largest agricultural engineering combine in the country.

The stand opposite the entrance of the Corn Exchange certainly had some advantages. "They catch all the bargains before we have a chance," said William Marriage, who had a stand nearer the back.

It was true Old Thomas' stand was a good observation post, he could greet every trading visitor to the Corn Exchange. Farmers threshed their corn in quantities of three to ten tons. They brought samples of their corn in small black sample bags. Many would call at his stand and show him their samples and ask what price he would offer. He well knew that his main function was to set a value on the sample, after which it would be hawked around the Exchange to try and better his offer. He thus seldom bought any corn very cheaply, though those of his customers who had large feeding stuff accounts would take a moderate price for their wheat to settle their accounts.

On this particular day the miller took a jaundiced view of buying wheat. It had been a wet harvest and most of the crop would require months of drying out in the stack before it would be in condition to grind. The samples on offer were far too damp to produce flour. Samuel had said, "mix the damp wheat with Canadian Number One Manitoba which is as dry as shot, and leave it on the barn floor. The dry Manitoba will absorb the moisture from the damp wheat so it will grind". The only drawback was, Manitoba had gone off the market. There was some transport trouble with the new crop and no-one knew exactly when more could be expected.

The Quaker Joseph Smith came up to Old Thomas' stand, "Good afternoon, Mr. Smith," greeted the farmer.

"Good afternoon, Mr. Smith," greeted the miller.

The sample of wheat he showed Old Thomas was nicely dressed and free from weed seeds and other impurities, and in spite of the wet harvest, was dry. Old Thomas knew that in those days Quakers were not sought after as tenants by the big landlords. Joe's father had managed to acquire the tenancy of a large farm from a Quaker brewer who had bought a country estate, Joe had tried to hire a farm on a neighbouring estate owned by the redoubtable 'Only'. But the Squire had asserted, "I like you very well, Joe, and I like your farming even better, but I like to see my tenants sitting in church on Sundays." Quaker Joe was no cap-toucher, nor was his father. A successful industrialist from the Midlands bought a mansion in Great Saling, the village where Joe's father had his home. The industrialist proposed to build a brick wall to enclose his park. The old deeds were vague about boundaries, particularly where a large green, which might have been a village green, or common land, joined the park. The newcomer consulted the old inhabitant, Joe's father, who strongly advised against the enclosure of the green. The deeds were further investigated and the industrialist wrote a note to Old Joe to inform him he intended to wall in the green the next week. The old Quaker replied formally as follows: "If thee sends thy men to build a wall to enclose the green next week, then my men shall pull thy wall down the week after." The 'thee' and 'thy' frightened the industrialist and the green at Saling is unenclosed to this day. This sort of thing did not help to get a tenancy of a farm and Joe had to buy land with borrowed money and pay high interest on it in hard times.

***

Jimmy Oldfield approached Thomas's stand with a sample of wheat. Jimmy was an old customer, who Old Thomas knew to be a mild sort of man whose nature was always to be pleasant. He had been churchwarden for years, and no Finchingfield social event took place without his help. He was a 'cap-toucher' all right. He lived at 'Oldsborough Manor'. As the village said, "a high-up address for a low-down place." It was no longer a Manor-house. That had been burned down about forty years ago and the landlord's estate carpenter had bodged up a mean little house from the ruin. More than half of the best land had been taken away and joined with Biggins Farm.

Old Thomas knew that Jimmy had been blessed with a jewel of a wife. Educated at Miss Moorcroft's school, she excelled as a capable housewife. Her eggs and butter paid the housekeeping bills and for such of her clothes as were not made with her own clever needle. Having no children, she indulged her tremendous energy and maternal instinct in rearing Jimmy's calves. She

11

could, and did, milk the cows when Jimmy and the stockman were busy at haytime and harvest. When the calves were sold in the autumn, the price realised was sufficient to pay Jimmy's rent.

Alas and alack, Jimmy's jewel suffered from an attack of colic (appendicitis today), which proved fatal, and Jimmy found himself a widower. After a suitable interval he did as other farmers had done in like case, he advertised for a housekeeper.

He counted himself fortunate to engage a lady, quite good looking, and also educated at the redoubtable Miss Moorcroft's school. Moreover she appeared to be possessed of ample private means. She had a large and impressive looking volume which was an illustrated catalogue from one of the new London mail order firms. Jimmy thought this was a very high class company, as all the prices in this beautifully illustrated volume were marked in guineas. It had long been recognised in the country that only 'gentlemen' dealt in guineas. Jimmy was not a little surprised and certainly appreciative when the new housekeeper, on her own volition, replaced his own chipped crockery with new dinner and tea services. This was followed by new cutlery.

Soon after, this lady of impeccable taste received, by passenger train, a very large box containing a hat described by Finchingfield as 'most as big as a rowin' boat', trimmed with an ostrich feather, and a voluminous feather boa to match. Jimmy regarded his market breeches with shame. Thanks to his late wife's skilful needle they were more patch than breech. He gave them to his horseman and invested not only in a new pair from the local tailor, but also yellow boots and buskins and a new billycock hat, all to keep up with this superior female who kept his house so well. He then visited his friend Tom Eaton, the coachbuilder, and purchased from him a fresh-painted secondhand Ralli cart and some silver-mounted harness lately belonging to Smasher Pile, before he broke his neck.

With his fresh clipped cob, Jimmy and his housekeeper made a brave sight as they drove to market. The village, however, with unfailing instinct, was sceptical. Doubts were expressed in 'The Swan' if she weren't a "high bough off a low bush".

Jimmy had no qualms in proposing to this beautiful and wealthy windfall. After proper hesitation, she accepted, and it appeared the only condition was that she be allowed to bring pictures, ornaments and some furniture from her old home. To this Jimmy readily agreed. He was somewhat shaken however to observe the large picture in the form of a text being hung over what was to be her side of the marriage bed. In a golden frame and with the huge letters embellished with orange blossom appeared the holy caption '*I Need Thee Every Hour*'. After giving the matter weighty consideration, Jimmy visited a junk shop when next attending market, and succeeded in hanging over his side of the bed a picture with a matching text spelt out in equally beautiful letters '*God Give Me Strength*'.

Harvest at last over, the marriage took place and the happy couple journeyed for their honeymoon. The first morning was taken up in selecting a large gold-mounted cameo brooch for the blushing bride. In the afternoon it rained.

"How shall we pass the time?" enquired the lady, observing the raindrops streaming down the window panes. Now Jimmy had paid for the cameo brooch with the money with which he expected to pay the Boarding House bill in Margate.

"I think, my dear," he suggested, "we should have a discussion on future financial arrangements for the household."

"Certainly, James," replied his beaming bride.

The minutes of this momentous conference have not survived. It became manifest that Jimmy had bought buckskin breeches, buskins and billycock hat, to say nothing of his fresh trap and harness, on credit in expectation of marrying a wealthy widow. She on her part had used the high-sounding address, 'Oldsborough Manor', to obtain credit with the mail order firm, thinking she would marry a substantial farmer. The honeymoon was cut short and the bride spent the remaining time crocheting a woollen tam-o'shanter. The new cameo brooch, the hat "most as big as a rowing boat' and the ostrich feather boa went into not so cold storage at the sign of the Three Golden Balls.

Jimmy thought he was in luck when he returned home to find the threshing tackle doing a short job on the next door farm, and able to move quickly to him, to thresh wheat to provide some much needed cash. He was blissfully unaware of the reason for it doing little work for his neighbour. It was found that the corn was so damp as to be unsaleable. "Leave it in the stack for a few months to dry out, " the merchants had advised.

So Jimmy Oldfield approached Old Thomas with some confidence.

"Good afternoon, Mr. Smith. Will you buy this lot of wheat?" he enquired, proffering the black sample bag filled with grain, which Thomas opened to examine the sample carefully. Wheat was apt to contain the seed of wild garlic (crows onions), exactly the same size and shape as a wheat kernel. No dressing machine of that date could separate it from wheat in bulk. When ground, it tainted the flour and later the bread. Thomas thrust his nose into the sample of grain and sniffed. It had no taint of onions nor was it musty. He then thrust two fingers into the bag, which the sample resisted. Good heavens, but it was damp! He then put a few grains into his mouth and chewed it.

"How many quarters have you got of this lot and what do you want to make of it?" he enquired.

"Forty-five quarters and I hope to make 26/-," replied Jimmy.

"I don't know whether I can grind it, it is very wet. It is not worth any such money. I will give you 22/-. "

"I can't afford to take 22/-."

"Well, try what other merchants or millers will give. I shan't be offended if you can beat my price."

Jimmy did not really wish to sell to Old Thomas, he thanked him for his offer and proceeded to other stands. He owed Old Thomas nearly as much money as the wheat could come to, and contra accounts were always reckoned up in settlement. Old Thomas, aware of the contra account, would have liked a settlement, but what could he do with the wheat? It would not grind as wet as it was. Samuel would mix it with Manitoba, but there was no prospect of obtaining any for weeks.

Jimmy tried every miller and merchant in the Corn Exchange, but could not get anyone else to offer any price at all. Damp wheat was a 'drug' on the market. He returned to Old Thomas' stand.

"Will you stand word at 22/-?" he enquired.

Not for the first time, Old Thomas discovered that he offered top price, this time for a problem lot of grain. He well knew what Samuel would say, but the old man thought of his contra account.

"Well, I suppose if you wish to sell this wheat I must try to buy it. When do you wish to send it in, or do you want me to collect it?"

"I want to send it in at once. There is another thing I must ask you. Will you leave my contra account for a few weeks? I have some good oats in stacks. Trade will improve when the winter draws on. I will sell you the oats for my account when I thresh."

"No, Mr. Oldfield. If you want me to take your damp wheat you must settle my account."

Forty years of dealing with farmers had given Old Thomas a small degree of hardness, in spite of his good nature. Giving 'strap' to those bakers years ago had done no one any good. 'Pay and be paid' was what young Samuel would say. The anxiety on Jimmy's face was plain to see. He was a nice chap and an old customer.

"I'll tell you what I will do," said Old Thomas, "You send the wheat in and I will deduct half my account and you can settle the other half when you thresh your oats. Take it or leave it."

Jimmy perforce took it.

'Nice cup of tea,' mused Old Thomas, 'can't collect my account without being clobbered with damp wheat which I do not want. Samuel will be complaining. Wish I could buy some dry wheat to mix with it.'

***

Old Thomas was then approached by a broad shouldered wiry young man with a pronounced Scottish accent, of Piddleybrook Farm. Would Thomas buy his wheat?

Old Thomas had observed the young Scot offering his sample to most of the other merchants on the Exchange. It was quite nice wheat and not too damp, but there was only a small quantity of it. After the usual haggling Thomas bought it for 23/3d per quarter. It needed the odd threepence to deal with the Scot and, as the miller suspected, to beat the price offered by other buyers.

Piddleybrook Farm in Finchingfield had become vacant after

old Perkin had died and was for a short time without a tenant. Then this Scottish bachelor had appeared. With few assets other than his brute strength and a native ability to live almost entirely on oatmeal, he had worked wonders with the farm. He was aided by a competent horseman who 'went with the farm', and four good horses, two of which he worked himself. The horseman's wife had 'done' for him as far as his simple habits and food required. The horseman had informed his new master which were the best fields, these were tackled first, the worst of the land was fallowed. It had been too late to plant a large area of wheat, but the Scot had produced a good crop of barley. Piddleybrook, being somewhat lighter land and therefore somewhat earlier, had escaped the worst of the weather afflicting the late harvest.

The Scot had threshed some barley immediately after harvest and sold it to a malster in Braintree. Soon after, he and his horseman set off with a four horse waggon load of corn to deliver to the malting. After discharging the load, the Scot was paid for it in sovereigns, as he had bargained. His first investment was in 'half a goblin' (half a gallon) of whisky, so he and his horseman could celebrate suitably the first sale of a crop which they had.produced with such prodigious labour and with such little sustenance. They then made their way the ten miles home to Finchingfield at three miles per hour with the four horses and waggon.

Arrived at the farm, the Scot gave much needed assistance to his horseman in housing the waggon and feeding the horses. He then invited him into the farmhouse for further celebration. How the night passed has not been recorded, but the Scot was wakened in the morning by loud groans from his horseman who was lying on the floor beside him. This was clearly an emergency requiring stimulant. The Scot found his empty glass and tilted the half gallon stone jar to re-charge it. In vain. The half gallon whisky bottle was empty!

He rushed to the horseman's cottage to get the horseman's wife to assist her husband. The provident arrival of the postman enabled a message to be sent to the village doctor telling him what had happened. The medico appeared in his gig as soon as maybe and proceeded to apply a stomach pump to the afflicted horseman. Alas it was too late. Too much of the whisky had got into his blood stream and the horseman died of alcohol poisoning. While all this was going on the Scot, who had consumed the lion's share of the whisky, took out a pair of horses and ploughed his acre of ground as though nothing untoward had happened.

***

Winterflood Legerton approached the stand. Old Thomas had known him for years, straight as a gun barrel, close as a clam, had come through a very hard school. He was a grandson of the 'onion seed kings' of Shalford, a small village four miles from Finchingfield. The 'onion seed kings' were two brothers who had acquired a fortune in hard times in the 1820s in a very simple way. Though possessed of some rather poor land they hit on a bright idea and developed it. By a process of selection they isolated some successful strains of onion, grew them in seed beds on their farm in the autumn and in spring distributed the young onion plants to cottagers over a wide district. All the cottagers were good gardeners; they had to be to augment their near starvation wages. They replanted the onions in their gardens, manured them with human excreta from their pail closets or privies and wood ash from the weekly bakings in their bread ovens. With this cultivation and fertilization, the onion plants produced wonderful seed heads. The cottagers hung up the seed heads under the eves of their thatched cottages until they were thoroughly dry, then knocked out the seed by hand. The seed was then collected by Winterflood's grandfather, who rewarded the growers with a shilling or two. Since it was the best onion seed in the country, they enjoyed a very profitable trade at little trouble and expense to themselves.

One of the onion seed kings was a bachelor. The other had one son. Reared in luxury and married to a genteel lady, the son had neither the ability nor the inclination and certainly not the opportunity to join in this essentially vulgar trade. He was put into Panfield Hall Farm in partnership with his brother-in-law. Time went by, the venture failed. The onion king then hired a 450 acre farm in partnership with his son. By that time there was

17

a grandson, Winterflood, aged 18, who would run the new farm for his incompetent father and tough grandfather. The old man died soon after, leaving a large fortune to his son and his half-share in the lease of the farm to his grandson. The son, who had never been allowed to have sole responsibility for any serious business, began to gamble in a big way, assisted by his brother-in-law. Within two years he was in financial difficulties and Winterflood was compelled to buy out his father's share of the lease with borrowed money. There he was, just 21 years old, with a 450 acre farm and no money. With rocklike thrift and dedicated application, he survived. Some time later he was fortunate in marrying a charming and competent wife possessed of a modest fortune.

He came up to Old Thomas's stand, "Afternoon, Mr. Smith. How is the corn trade?"

"Bad! There is no wheat dry enough to thresh. If I buy any, I can't grind it".

"Dear, dear: What is the matter with you? I seem to remember a song 'There was a jolly miller once, Lived on the River Dee'. If I don't make a mistake the Dee is in Scotland where they have a lot more rain than we get hereabouts. I shall have to try and cheer you up."

"You may be right about Scottish rain. However much they have there doesn't make us dry here. The song says most particularly that the miller on the Dee was only jolly once. If you want to cheer me up, tell me where there is some good dry wheat."

"I can do just that. My neighbour, Nick Oakes, has two hundred quarters of last year's wheat lying in a heap on his barn floor. That ought to be dry enough. We had a fine harvest last year and he left it in the stack 'til April, rats or no rats. I don't know if he will sell it though. He is loaded with money. "

"Ah, yes. Old Nick, the chap who married a succession of well-endowed widows and inherited their money. They say he keeps a quarter of a peck of sovereigns in the house and sometimes when he is drunk he will shoot them out on the hearthrug and roll in them. It must be nice to have a wealthy neighbour," chuckled Old Thomas.

"It is not," replied Winterflood, "he took to keeping sows and pigs, to eat some barley he could not sell. They roamed all over the parish. One old sow got into twenty acres of my beans, went wild and had her litter in the middle."

"What did you do about it?" asked the miller.

"Shot her."

"Bit rash wasn't it?"

"There was a flock of rooks on the beans, I loaded my gun, crept up a water furrow on all fours to get near enough to shoot one, came across the sow and litter. She came for me, wild as could be, I had to shoot her in self defence."

"Is Nick at market to-day?" asked Old Thomas.

"I saw him in the cattle market, but he will be at the White Hart by now, most likely playing cards with the flash set. If you want to have a deal with him you call on him on a Monday morning."

"I'll do that. Thanks for the tip, old friend. Good-day to you."

II

BUSINESS IN HARD TIMES.

A feature of the Essex farm was a huge thatched barn. The barn at Coleman's, the home of Nick Oakes, was just such a building, it consisted of eight bays with two porches which were, as always, east and west to catch the prevailing wind. This carried the chaff away when the corn had been threshed by flail. The barns were built for loose barley and sheaves of wheat which had been reaped with a sickle. It was usual practice when filling the inside stack of corn (mow), to compact it to increase the barn capacity. This was done by leading an old horse round the top. The end of those horses was frequently strained tendons in the front legs. It was customary when the stack was high, to let the old horse down on to a heap of straw at the end of the day. The horse was steadied down by a rope tied to its tail and held by the men at the top of the stack. The farm workers were prone to be either wearied by the day's harvest or dulled by having had too much beer, the heap of straw was sometimes inadequate and the men up top likely to let the rope on the horses's tail slip. Thus the horse came down with a bump and jarred its tendons. At Temple Barns they once got a horse cast near the roof of a gigantic barn, that is to say, it slipped over near the roof and lay more on its back than on its belly and was unable to get up. It was only rescued by cutting a hole in the barn roof.

The following Monday morning Old Thomas drove up to Coleman's Farm in his trap pulled by Polly, into the spacious stable yard, and knocked at the brewhouse door of the farmhouse. His knock was answered by a kitchenmaid who conveyed the information of a caller to her fearsome master. He came scowling to the door.

"Good morning, miller. What brings you here?"

"Good morning, Mr. Oakes. I hear you have some old wheat in your barn. I thought I might buy it from you."

"I have some old wheat, but I never told anyone I wanted to sell."

"May I have a look?"

"You can if you like but I won't sell it to you."

He led Old Thomas to the huge thatched barn, opened the porch doors. Inside a vast heap of golden grain was revealed. Old Thomas's eyes popped. He thrust his hand into the heap. As he expected, his arm went in up to his elbow. He put some grain into his mouth and tried to chew it. Hard and dry as a bullet. He smelt a handful. Not a trace of mustiness.

"I should like to buy this wheat from you, Mr. Oakes. I would give you a fair price. How about thirty shillings a quarter. I find the sacks and collect."

"I don't want to sell. You have wasted your time driving up here this morning. Can you tell me any one reason why I should sell this wheat to you?"

"Yes, I can. When you need oats for your horses, you send word to my mill, and my man delivers them to you. For years you have had what you needed at a fair price. I never refused to sell to you, or your horses might have gone hungry. I need this wheat just as your horses have needed my oats. Isn't that a good reason for selling it to me?"

Nick regarded the miller with a baleful eye and for once was at a loss for an answer.

"I'm d - d if you are not the only honest miller I ever knew or ever heard of . Come to think on it, I'm d - d if there is not a good reason for a deal. I hear your son has been breaking-in a thoroughbred colt for a friend of mine. He told me he was having it back this month. I have a four-year-old thoroughbred I want worked. If your son will break him in, I will sell you the d - d wheat".

"I am afraid I cannot speak for Frank. He does what he likes. As he is always doing it hard, and it's gainful employment, I leave him alone," replied the cautious father.

"Ho, but he could not take a colt if you did not find him a stable. If your son will take my colt and get him handy, I will pay what you charge, and sell you the wheat".

"Well, Mr. Oakes, I will see what I can do. I dare say I can come to some arrangement. I have some empty sacks in my trap. I could leave them. If you get them filled I could pick up a load on Thursday, when my man is delivering in this district. I will send some more empty sacks then."

"You do that. I hope you like the wheat, and your son will like my colt. Good day to you, miller."

"Good day to you, Mr. Oakes."

For the first time in his life Old Thomas was able to please both his sons at a stroke. Samuel was delighted to have some vital dry wheat for the flour trade and Frank was delighted to have another colt to handle.

***

The young horse was led to the mill by Mr. Oakes's tiny groom. "All he wants now is work," he told Frank, "Mr. Oakes will never let a colt do a stroke till it is four years old, to let the legs get hard. I should have worked him during the summer but the Gov'nor wouldn't let me. He said hard ground was not good for young horses to work on, or young men to fall on."

"I can't see you falling off and I never heard of Mr. Oakes ever considering anyone else's comfort or safety. Why are you not breaking the horse yourself?" asked young Frank.

"I am leaving. That is why the colt has come to you. The horseman's son is going to look after the nags. He can feed the horses well enough, but he is no horseman. Sits a horse like a sack of taters!'

"How come you to be leaving. Is Mr. Oakes a bad master?"

"He always treated me well enough. My father was head lad to Penn, the Newmarket trainer. I could never get on with my dad, so I took this job. Dad died in the summer and Penn offered me his place. Mr. Oakes never complained at all. Seemed pleased for me to better myself."

"Ah, good luck," said Frank.

"It will be better in Newmarket. You never know what the Guv'nor will do next. A few weeks ago at the end of a night's drinking he got the idea someone was in the stable trying to steal his horse. He always keeps a loaded gun in his house, he has a lot of money there. It was moonlight, he took his gun and felt all over his horses to see if they was all there. They was, so he looked round the back of the house. Over the top of the garden wall he thought he could see two eyes staring at him so he let off a barrel and went back to bed. Come the morning he hollered at me from the bedroom window and asked if the horses was alright. I told him they was. He then asked me if I noticed anything wrong. I said no, but Sandy Tom cat lay dead in the road outside the farm."

"Ah," said Frank, "well, Cheerio, all the best," and he led the prancing colt firmly to a stable.

***

Harry Broyd was a cattle dealer, son of a cattle dealer of large family and small fortune. With little money, Harry determined to follow his father's calling if not his footsteps. He had from early boyhood developed a very good 'eye' for all livestock; he travelled the country buying and selling small lots from small farmers. The livestock dealer of that age was notoriously sly and sharp to a degree of dishonesty. Harry tried to give a fair price when buying, and tried to sell stock which would thrive and do well for his customers. He had received an early check in his chosen trade. His pony and cart, essential to transport him to the local markets and his customers around the countryside, had been stolen. The farmers had been sorry for the youthful dealer's misfortune, they collected a sum of money, bought him a fresh and even better driving cob and square bucked cart. (The 'buck' of a cart was its body). Frank Smith had subscribed a sovereign.

Harry had been most grateful, but his resolution to repay his helpers and friends did not blunt his determination to find the horse-thief. Pursuing his own enquiries he tracked his lost property through London to Kent, where the horse had been killed and boiled up for horse grease in a knacker's yard. The cart was broken to provide fuel for the gigantic boiling copper. The knackers had neglected to burn the spokes which had been freshly painted at Tom Eaton's. His man had a special way of painting gold flashes on the spokes where they joined the hub. Harry was able to identify, and swear to them. The thief, a gipsy, was arrested and tried. He was found guilty and given seven years penal servitude.

Frank was walking up to the windmill to check the millstones when Harry drove up in his new cart.

"'morning, Frank. I want to buy four weaned pigs worth the

23

money," he called, "it must be eight weeks since that sow I sold you for nothing pigged down."

"You always want to buy things 'worth the money," laughed Frank going up to the cart, "I have weaned the litter but thought of feeding them on."

"You sell me four, it will give the others a little more room to feed and lay down."

"What do you want them for?"

"The Squire wants two to eat up the refuse from his houseful of servants. I am buying two hogs from Sam Allen. I have to send him two weaners to take their place."

"Aha, they say Sam is never without two pigs in the stye in his cottage garden, nor without a sovereign in his pocket, none the more for being a farm worker at fifteen shillings a week and having ten children. Come on over to the shed and see what I've got."

"Right. They say Sam gives his wife a hiding every time she is in the family way," gossiped Harry.

"She's a good woman," commented Frank, "she takes all those children gleaning, stone picking and potato picking. She never buys any bread. They bring their gleaned wheat here to grind or have a regular sack of flour. She bakes the bread every week. The children all turn out to church respectable on Sundays."

"She weren't feeling very pleasant when I called this week. She'd run a bush [thorn] into the joint of her thumb when heating the bread oven with a bush faggot, her hand was poisoned and painful. You talk about her family gleaning! They picked up most a ton of acorns in the Squire's park last year to give to Sam's pigs. Strong hogs will do well on acorns and taters."

Harry looked at the pen of pigs in the shed, poking them with his stick. After the usual haggling, he bought four, marking them by cutting the hair off the ends of their tails with scissors.

"How about a beer, Harry?" asked Frank, impulsively.

"Thanks, don't mind if I do," replied the surprised young man.

They went back across the yard, through the wicket gate into the garden and in by the front door to the dining room without

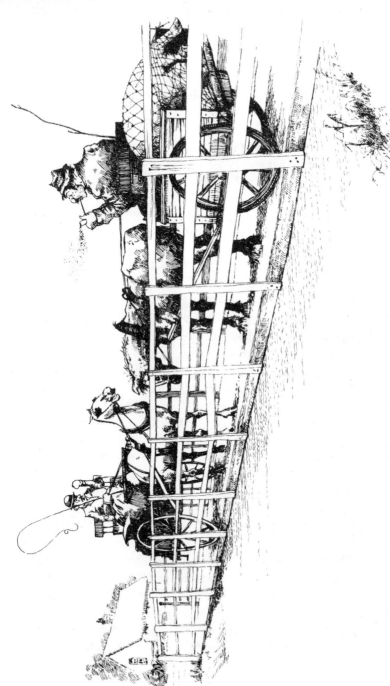

'None of both of them would give way'

being seen.

"Have a seat," said Harry, pointing to the large black horsehair chair by the hearth, "hang on a minute, I'll fetch some beer." Back he came with two tankards of homebrew and gave one to Harry, then sprawled back on to the black covered chair on the other side of the hearth, "Cheers," he exclaimed.

"Did I see Nick Oakes' groom going out of your yard, Frank? You want to be careful if you have any dealings with old Nick."

"I am not dealing with him. He sent me a hunter colt to break. His groom is leaving."

"My father met old Nick on Shoving Bridge last week. The ford was blocked by Mynot's timber. You know the bridge isn't wide enough for two?"

"They should have built it wider so it took the timber carriage," said Frank.

"Old Nick comes along one side with his clipped highstepper with silver plated harness and silver mounted whip. Dad, in his pony float with an old sow under a pig net, his sorry old cob and harness tied up with string, comes up the other side. They met in the middle of the bridge."

Frank laughed, Harry went on, "'out of my way Broyd' shouted Old Nick, 'I've got to catch the bank'. 'If yer please, Mr. Oakes, will you git out of my way, I've got to take this here sow to Jiggles Farm to catch the boar', hollers Dad. 'Damn you that I won't' shouts Old Nick."

"Lor, so what happened?" Frank re-filled the tankards.

"Shouts Dad, 'If yer was the Devil I could not back my horse, he's chink backed.'"

"Ah, that darned affliction of the spine preventing a horse from reversing," said Frank.

"Yes. 'If you don't get out of my way I will report you to the police and summons you' bellows Old Nick. Neither both of 'em would give way. Dad fills his pipe with shag and puffs away, the wind took the smoke to Old Nick, it stank worse than his pig-cart. Nick's horse wouldn't stand still. They sat there swearing at each other all afternoon. If it hadn't been for that hailstorm they'd still be there. The rain came down just in time, Dad was on his last pipeful of tobacco. The old sow had most 'gone off' before she reached the boar."

"Serves Old Nick right."

"Did you hear about him at Colchester a couple of weeks ago?"

"No, have some more beer." The two young men tipped it back.

"Old Nick thought he'd put up at Cup's Hotel for the week-end. They had a new up-and-coming waitress in the dining room. Nick made her acquaintance well enough at lunch for her to sit on his knee."

"The man shall have his mare," laughed Frank.

" 'e slipped 'er a five pund note to come to 'is room after lights out! "

"The old devil."

"Alas, an afternoon's reflection by the girl produced the conclusion she liked the fee better than the prospect of earning it! She sub-let the contract to a sixty-year-old potato peeler."

"I don't believe it!" exclaimed Frank.

"It's true. Nick got down to cards with his friends after dinner. They noticed he was dosing himself up with brandy. He left the card room early and called for his chamber candlestick. When he entered the bedroom he perceived, as expected, the bed was occupied. Drunk or sober he always expects to get his money's worth! He strips off the bedclothes to behold this dark eyed Venus in her night attire (or without her night attire). Even the dim light of the candle was enough to show 'im 'e'd been 'done'. He bellowed and 'e bellowed that crone cows were to be had in the market for £3 a piece, where the services of drovers were provided to beat them with sticks and drive them to the slaughter house."

The door opened. It was Old Thomas and Samuel.

"Frank! I thought you were up at the mill! What are you doing here?" demanded Old Thomas.

"Beg pardon, sir. Best be off," replied the flustered Harry who fled the room like a hunted fox.

"What are you doing with the worker's beer?" demanded Samuel.

"I thought the Minister, your mother and I had warned you

enough of the evils of drink," exclaimed Old Thomas.

"I am sorry, father. Harry has just bought a couple of weaners. Tell mother I shall not be in for lunch. I'll see to the millstones straight away."

Somewhat flushed and slightly unsteadily Frank crossed the room, stuffed his copy of his favourite play, *The Taming of the Shrew*, into his jacket pocket and left as quickly as possible.

***

Every week William Newman would send a cartload of beans and barley to the mill to grind for his stock and some oats to crush for his horses. William was a sharpish customer, he kept 'The Vine' in Finchingfield, ran a building business and had a modest farm. It was always a scandal that he paid all his men in his pub on a Friday night, hoping they would spend as much of it as possible on beer before they left. It was for men like him that Parliament was proposing to pass a law prohibiting the payment of wages in a public house.

William's grist was always carted to the mill by Ben, his odd job man. Ben had a crippled foot and could not do a full man's work. He arrived at the mill with beans which were in very large six bushel sacks, though they were in nineteen-stone lots, the weight of four bushels.

"You will have to unload these b - - beans," Ben demanded, "Frank, you're as strong as a giant and I'm as weak as a rat. Nineteen stone is plenty for any man, but these here beans in these six-bushel sacks appear half as heavy again."

As Frank unloaded the exceedingly awkward heavy sacks he remarked that the six bushel sacks were new and marked with William's name.

"They be covetous men's sacks," explained Ben, "they may well bear William Newman's name. Everybody in Finchingfield calls him 'Swallow-all Newman'. He sells his barley to the malster in Braintree. When he sends in a supply, he brings back a load of malt culms (the dried shoots of barley after the malt has been made). He found they would always fill his sacks full if he gave the malting foreman a drink. So he had these d - d awkward six-bushel sacks made to send his barley in and be returned full with malt culms."

A few Sundays later Frank heard poor Ben had met some friends in a pub other than 'The Vine'. They treated Ben to some 'Old and Strong', a fatal brew for an empty stomach. Returning unsteadily to his home, he encountered his employer in the village street. He addressed him as follows: "Good afternoon, Mr. Swallow-All. I have just seen Benson, the sackmaker. He wants to make you some eight-bushel sacks. I told him it would not do any good because ten-bushel sacks would not hold enough for you." Ben was sacked on the spot but from then on Newman was known as Swallow-all Newman.

At market the next week Newman brought his grinding account to settle. He placed his cheque book and account on Old Thomas's stand, "How much discount are you going to allow me off my account?" he demanded.

"You can take two and a half per cent," replied Old Thomas.

"I think I ought to have five. You deduct four pounds in weight for every sack of meal you grind for me."

"Mr. Newman, if I put a sack of sixteen stones of your corn through my mill it will waste about four pounds in grinding, whether it be dust or steam. I cannot clean my stones down nor sweep out my bin for every customer I have, or I should have the mill stopped half the time. Weighing your corn in, and meal out, protects me and protects you. There is no big profit out of grist on which I can allow you more discount."

William wrote his cheque with ill grace, to which Old Thomas was completely indifferent.

***

About the same time, a fresh industry appeared in the Corn Exchange. It happened that the chemist across the road became interested in bees. He read in a pamphlet that:

A swarm of bees in May
Is worth a load of hay.
A swarm of bees in June
Is worth a silver spoon.
A swarm of bees in July
Isn't worth a fly.

The chemist let it be known he would give a sovereign for a good swarm. It was not long before a youth appeared with a

29

swarm in a straw skep on a board. The chemist, to make sure he was getting twenty shilling's worth, took the skep off the board and looked inside. Out flew a bee and stung him on the nose. He dropped the skep. He and the youth ran for their lives. They were not stung much, but the swarm escaped and took up its abode in the Corn Exchange roof. There the bees remained for years. They were apparently of no inconvenience to the stand holders. Perhaps these industrious insects recognised some kindred spirits in the visitors to the Corn Exchange. Both insect and man were addicted to incredible labour for scant reward.

Years later when the Corn Exchange roof needed repairing the same chemist supplied some poison to get rid of the uninvited guests.

***

One market day, Alfred Byford came up to the stand and passed the time of day with Old Thomas. Alfred was another one notoriously 'close', even in a close-fisted fraternity. He had purchased a new reaping machine which had recently been developed. This would cut the corn and replaced mowing with a scythe, but the sheaves still had to be tied by hand. After the machine had cut forty of Alfred's eighty acres successfully he had it packed away in the cart lodge and his harvest gang reverted to scythes.

"Why can't we continue with the reaper?" enquired his nephew who had come to assist in the harvest.

"Because I have set it up till next year. If it cuts another forty acres it will wear out twice as fast."

Old Thomas and Alfred observed a tall good-looking man enter the Corn Exchange. He wore a top hat at an important angle. His high starched collar was held together by a brightly coloured cravat; this in turn was fastened with a gold pin displaying a flashing stone which might have been a diamond. His cutaway coat displayed an impeccable 'kerchief in his breast pocket. He wore lemon coloured gloves and carried a gold mounted cane.

Alfred was struck by the appearance of this important and fashionable figure.

"See there Thomas," he remarked, "looks like we have a

member of the House of Lords come to market today!"

"Lord be hanged: You ought to know who that is, he came from Shalford. That's Winterflood's brother, Samuel Legerton, the other grandson of the Onion Seed Kings. He's in the seed trade, has a London seed business. He comes down here to put turnip seed out to farmers to grow. He always comes to the country in his London clothes to show his brother up. He looks down on his country relations."

"Does he indeed! Winterflood is good enough for most anyone to look up to. I would rather deal with he than this dressed up toff."

The two men were joined by a third who lived in Shalford.

"Was there not some talk about this Sam and Squire's daughter?" enquired Alfred.

"Indeed there was," replied the Shalford man, "Samuel and his other brother, who was a powerful young minister in the Chapel somewhere or other, both fell in love with the Squire's daughter. The Squire could not 'come up' with they; made some talk about their courtship stinking of onions, none the more for being two fine looking young men. The Squire took and married his daughter to a Doctor, which was supposed to be more genteel. Like other young married women, she soon had several children and she engaged a nursery governess to help look after them. The Doctor took up with the nursery governess and, when people began to talk, he bought a practice in Ireland and they all removed over to there. Once across the water, he took and poisoned his wife with arsenic and married the governess. They might have lived happy ever after, only he was arrested and tried and hung not so long ago. The other Sunday, Samuel was walking along the lane near his home, in full fig as he is now, when he came face to face with the Squire! Samuel took off his hat, 'Good afternoon Squire, this is a very fortunate meeting. There is a question I have long wished to ask you; how do you reckon the smell of arsenic compares with the stink of onions?'"

"I heard they very nigh got to boxing. If they did not quite get to blows they had some very high words," chuckled Old Thomas.

His attention was caught by another dressed up customer,

"Well, Legerton has found a farmer dressed to match him. I have not seen Jack Metson in a top hat and frock coat before. He has come a long way since he was a farm worker." The farmers' heads turned to look.

"Good luck to him," said Old Thomas, "he has always worked as hard as any. He may be hard and close, but he is as straight as a gun barrel. He hired a field which no one else would have, borrowed a pair of horses from his boss to work it. It was in a poor state so he grew a crop of barley and undersowed with clover."

No smallholder had been able to afford this crop, before Jack Metson sold the first cut of clover as it stood to a neighbour to make into hay. He fluked a good crop of seed with the second cut, and that in a year when clover-seed was worth a lot of money. It made enough for him to hire a farm. This he worked with such success it was not long before he bought a sizeable farm. Proving himself credit worthy, Jack had now bought more than a thousand acres. Never having had much money of his own, he had not minded how much he borrowed of other peoples'. His crops were always above average and his cultivations forward in any season. Recently a neighbour chided him for sporting a frock coat and top hat. Jack had replied, "If a commercial traveller selling patent cattle medicines can call on me in top hat and cutaway coat, I am making a poor fist of farming a thousand acres if I can't turn myself out as well as him."

***

On another occasion an old woman came up to Thomas's stand and offered a sample of feeding beans. Few women ever visited the Corn Exchange. Thomas knew all about this one. Her face was deeply lined and the colour of folded leather. Her bitter expression and harsh manner frightened her neighbour's children, who thought she was a witch. She had been married to a good-for-nothing cattle dealer and lived at Tilekiln Farm. She had two sons. One was a fine lad who saw after the farm. The other accompanied his father to markets and drove the cattle he purchased to his client's farms. The dealer often came home late and drunk. He often beat his wife with an 'ash' stick, with which he beat his bullocks at market.

The time came when the farming son could stand no more of his mother being beaten. He told his father that if he ever again saw him hit his mother with a stick, he would shoot him.

One night the young man was seeing after a cow having a calf in the byre when he heard his mother scream. Her husband was beating her. The young man ran to the house, picked up his muzzle-loading gun, put in a charge of powder and rammed it home with a wad. He then put in a charge of shot and rammed that home with a wad. He then shot his father. He repeated the process of loading the ancient gun and shot himself. He was buried at midnight and a man who later became Frank's horseman drove the horses and hearse.

Another exception who visited the Corn Exchange was Mrs. Jones. She had married a hard working young butcher and used to help in the shop. Times were very hard in the countryside. The butcher was better at work in his shop than in his office. Some of his customers just would not or could not pay. The time came when he had not the wherewithal to pay for meat 'on the hoof'. He must have gone nearly mad with anxiety, for he stole and slaughtered a sheep and was caught. For this offence he was sentenced to two year's imprisonment. Now everyone was sorry for the wife who had a young family to support and the farmers got together to help her. They not only gave her limited credit for bullocks, pigs and sheep, but also they gave her their custom. Assisted by a faithful journeyman she kept the shop going. When her husband had served his sentence, he returned to a thriving business which continued for nearly a hundred years.

***

Another recipient of much needed help was John Gilbey. He existed on a small farm appropriately named Foul Slough. One July the grandfather of all thunderstorms broke across his farm. A stroke of lightning killed his only two old farm horses. The stems of his sparse corn crop were completely cut off by driving hail, his disaster was complete. It was about the time of the launching of a new London daily newspaper which somehow heard of the tragedy and poor old John made the headlines. Thanks to the London newspaper, the Squire inaugurated a disaster fund for John's benefit, so well supported that it grossed more than treble the amount the poorish crop would have realised without the storm. It would have enabled John to replace his old worn-out horses with pedigree shires. But the storm also affected John's wife. She so far increased her authority that, when the disaster fund was paid out, she insisted that they cleared out of Foul Slough Farm and took the 'Pig and Whistle'. Here they presumably lived happily ever after, as, with enough gin inside her, she had been heard to say that the only thing wrong with the hailstorm was that it did not come twenty years sooner!

III

THE FAMILY FARM, 1887

A few weeks later the threshing tackle appeared at the family farm, Claypit Hall, between Bardfield and Finchingfield, which was farmed by Old Thomas's elder brother Mathew. This farm had generally produced wheat of the best quality, but Thomas had not purchased any for three years. The reason? He was owed a very hefty bill for milling and feeding stuff and his brother was afraid of a contra account. It would take more than the poor crop his brother had grown this year to settle with his patient milling brother. As when he had been driving to market, Old Thomas reflected that things did not seem to work out very well in their family. His descent through a sequence of younger sons had been their misfortune, and this was aggravated by the family hot temper. His own father had been disinherited because of an outburst of temper, leading to Thomas becoming a miller, and the family farm going to Mathew, who certainly did not have what it takes to be a success as a farmer. He did everything wrong that could be done wrong on his good little farm. Young Frank would complain that if you went to see him on a fine day in spring when all the field work should be going full steam ahead, Uncle Mathew would be sure to be away in the village, his horses tied up in the stable and his workers messing about doing 'no account' odd jobs. Easy going and interested in everyone's business except his own, Mathew's farm ran out to weeds, all in view from the top of the windmill. It was a constant source of fury to Frank.

Mathew's only son, Martin, was no help on the farm either. He enjoyed his long evenings at the local pub more than his short days of work on the farm, when he was there! He was often absent. He was a fine shot and regularly invited to shooting parties to help bring down a respectable bag. Martin infuriated young Frank by boasting of the foxes he had shot.

In 1887 Queen Victoria had her Jubilee. There had been a grand fête in the village to celebrate. Martin was organiser of the sports events - a great success. After it was all over, he and his friends repaired to the 'Three Horseshoes' with more than their usual thirst, to drink the Queen's health with the specially strong Jubilee ale which had been brewed for the happy day.

In the pub were two loonies. They were two brothers of great strength and very uncertain temper, not 'right' in the head and feared by all the village, or nearly all. When the Queen's health was called, they made a disparaging and disrespectful remark about Her Revered Majesty. Now Martin was short and square. What he lacked in inches he made up for with pugnacity. He immediately demanded that the two loonies stand up and drink the Queen's health or leave the bar. They replied with invective. Such was the strength of Martin's patriotism, and maybe the strength of the Jubilee ale, that he offed with his coat, spat on his hands and went into battle. An homeric fight ended with the two loonies in the road and Martin very much the worse for wear, back in the bar and thirstier than ever. His thirst was as far as possible assuaged by copious draughts of the renowned Jubilee brew. Time was at length called. Martin had to make his way home as best he could. The lane to his home led past the cottage where the loonies lived with their widowed mother. Pausing opposite the gate, his blood boiled afresh at the affront to Her Majesty by his late antagonists. He came to the conclusion that the punishment he had administered was not sufficient for the offence. Further chastisement was certainly needed. He therefore burst into the cottage with this laudable object in view. Unfortunately for Martin, the loonies' mother came to their rescue with a heavy iron poker.

The next morning at five o'clock when the horseman came to work, he found Martin lying senseless in the road. He went to the farm, got his horses in from the meadow, harnessed one of them to a dung tumbrel, and went to cart him home. Martin, however, had a very hard head. He recovered in time to enable him to drink a pint of 'homebrew' for a late breakfast, which was said to have 'suited' him better than the strong Jubilee ale.

This might have been the end of the story, but it was not to be. A month later the loonies expressed their gratitude to their mother for rescuing them from Martin by cutting her throat. They subsequently became guests of her denigrated Majesty in

Broadmoor for the rest of their days.

***

Old Thomas did not see what could be done about the family farm but it was doubtful if things could go on much longer as they were in that quarter.

On his stand at the Corn Exchange he was talking to young Bates when his brother came past carrying a sample of corn. Bates had been apprenticed to Old Thomas, and had now progressed to assistant to William Marriage, the miller of Chelmsford. "I see your brother Mathew had a sample of corn to sell," said Bates, "Colleridges have their eye on him. They say he has not paid their coal and seed account for three years. When they learn who he sells his corn to, they are going to put a garnishee on it and collect the money."

"Say that again," demanded Old Thomas.

Bates repeated the gossip.

"Will you do something for me?" asked Old Thomas.

"Certainly I will if I can."

"My brother will most likely offer his wheat to William Marriage. Will you ask him to buy it for me? He may have to give a shilling a quarter more than it is worth, but whatever he gives I will give him a shilling a quarter profit and collect it from the farm. You stay on Mr Marriage's stand and when the deal is through, give me the wink."

Old Thomas, watching out of the corner of his eye, saw his brother approach Marriage's stand and proffer a sample of corn. He observed the signs of the inevitable haggling and saw Marriage hand over what might be a 'bought' note and retain the sample of corn. Old Thomas caught the eye of Bates, who winked perceptibly.

Old Thomas immediately left the Corn Exchange and repaired to the office of the notorious lawyer, Fred Smoothy. Fred was as tough as they come. He had given the miller sound advice when the bakers had got into his debt, but the advice had not been taken soon enough. Thomas was shown into the lawyer's office and Smoothy asked what he could do for him. Old Thomas explained in detail the sorry state of affairs between himself and his brother; he explained about the wheat deal and

37

the imminent danger of the garnishee.

Smoothy advised as follows: "If there is going to be a garnishee it had better come from you. I will make one out at once, and serve on Marriage before Colleridge's get a chance with theirs'. Marriage can hold the wheat for a time, and you can sort everything out with your brother later".

"I can't do that! It may be the cause of breaking him. I can't bankrupt my own brother. What will become of him? What will become of Martin?"

"It will not be you who breaks your brother, but the debit balance of his liabilities against his assets. Your brother is a widower, I believe. He can go and live with your widowed sister in Finchingfield. I handled her husband's estate and she has enough and to spare to keep two in comfort. As for Martin, if he is man enough to thrash those two loonies, as I heard, he is man enough to earn some sort of living. You are not responsible for the way your brother conducts his business. If he is insolvent, you cannot help him. I have advised you on debtors before and you did not take my advice. It looks like a case of your brother calling a meeting of his creditors. We will find out what he owes and what his assets amount to. You will have a trump card with the garnishee on his wheat. An offer to the creditors on your behalf and you could take over the farm by a deed of arrangement. I might even make a good thing of it for you".

So began a lengthy process Old Thomas would be glad to forget, though in the end, the lawyer claimed, it was best for everyone. Mathew went to live with his sister. This lady was the widow of a hard working builder. Thirty years of expert husband management had not saved him from falling off a scaffold and breaking his neck, but it had provided experience sufficient to cope with Mathew.
She provided him with enough money to drink with his friends at 'The Gate', but not enough to stand them a round. This salubrious hostelry was under the sign of a gate on which was spelled 'This Gate hangs high/ And hinders none,/ Refresh and pay/ And travel on.'

Mathew did sometimes travel on to 'The Vine' kept by his in-law. There he was wont to purvey his unwelcome advice on the conduct of the host's small farm in exchange for a very unwilling free pint of brown and old. These excursions enabled his sister to play the organ at Evensong and preside at a sewing party currently embroidering a set of church hassocks. Thus, Mathew had time for everyone's business without embarrassing his own. This satisfied him. His sister got a man about the house without the discomfort of marriage, that suited her.

Martin got a job as bouncer at a London hotel. That suited him, though whenever he had time off he returned to the farm and walked the fields with a gun, always bagging hares and partridges when in season.

The delighted Frank could see the prospect of working on and managing the family farm, Claypit Hall. That suited him, notwithstanding Old Thomas's dictum that he must first receive some apprentice instruction. Old Thomas was buoyed up with the hope of Frank growing the perfect milling wheat even if Samuel would have the privilege of grinding it into flour.

Samuel took the milling business on, and married. He had already made plans for equipping the mill with a set of roller mills and an oil engineto grind his precious Manitoba wheat. Old Thomas removed to Claypit Hall and so left his beloved mill.

If Smoothy thought that was best for Old Thomas, he could not see how, his bank overdraft was more astronomic than ever. But Smoothy said he could worry about what he owed the bank instead of what his brother owed him. The lawyer had certainly been tough and had won against the other creditors all along the line. They had been glad to take the offer Smoothy had made on behalf of Old Thomas to pay part off their bills, and glad to see him take the farm over with Frank.

***

Smoothy was, by marriage, a relation of the Smiths. One of the family had once called on him at his office. "What can I do for you Nathaniel?" he had enquired after the exchange of civilities.

"I want to borrow three thousand pounds till after the harvest. I wondered if you, or one of your clients, could lend it to me?"

Knowing his man, the lawyer asked what security Nathaniel could give for £3,000. He thought about this for a moment.

"I could come and live with you," he offered.

"To be sure you could," replied Smoothy.

He walked across his office and unlocked the door to the strong-room, "You come and get in here then I will lend you three thousand pounds," quipped the wise old lawyer.

***

Butcher's shops in those days were equipped with 'stable' doors, that is to say, a door cut in half so the top half could be kept open to let in much needed ventilation. The sly dogs of town, and country too, would jump over the bottom door and if the shop were unattended would help themselves to a joint of meat. Walter Nash once spied a dog making off with a leg of his mutton. The dog was soon out of sight, but Walter recognised it. He sent the owner a bill for six shillings and eightpence, which was indignantly rejected. Nash put the dispute in Smoothy's hands. In due course the butcher received a note to advise him of his lawyer's success and enclosing the account which read:

> To costs of claiming for leg of mutton: 6/8d
> By payment by defendant for leg of mutton: 6/8d
> Settled with thanks. P.Smoothy.

***

One Sunday morning George Fitch, a horseman of Finchingfield, walked the ten miles to Braintree to consult the lawyer on a pressing and weighty matter. After George's payment of the 6/8d fee, nearly half his week's wages, the lawyer asked his client what he could do for him.

"Well, sir, I want ye ter tell me who be the master in my house, me or my missis?"

Smoothy considered the matter.

"You are undoubtedly the master, George. However, since you come to me for advice, I advise you never to forget that your wife is mistress".

George then walked the ten miles home considering how he could put this expensive advice to practical effect.

***

In order to qualify for the management of the family farm, Frank was sent for a year's apprenticeship with a successful farmer. This man was a not-so-young widower who 'took an egg beaten up in a stiffish brandy for a nightcap every night'. He was one of the few men who had tried, albeit unsuccessfully, to stop three horses bolting with a Cambridge roller and lived to tell the tale. A Cambridge roller, used to crush clods on arable fields, weighed about a ton. It consisted of a large number of cast iron rings mounted on a shaft and fixed to a frame. A team of three horses was needed, one harnessed in shafts in the centre of the frame, with a horse 'in chains' on either side. The shaft horse was the only means of applying brakes to the roller. If the two outside horses bolted with fright, they were too strong for the shaft horse to stop the roll. Those who tried to stop horses bolting with a rib roll were invariably run over by the horses and roller and killed - all except the brandy drinker.

Unfortunately he combined the instincts of a bully with the necessary determination to make his farming succeed. Frank could and did acquire the latter, but was an unsuitable client to be on the receiving end of the former. The old martinet practised his hectoring abuse on his giant apprentice, who had inherited a full share of the family temper. Frank never answered back, but it is said that looks can speak louder than words. The old man first became nervous, and then frightened of his apprentice. When Frank requested leave of absence to attend the funeral of a near relative, it was curtly given with instruction not to return. Nevertheless Frank had been pupil long enough to learn the importance of efficiency and determination, and that it was necessary to have the full co-operation of the farm workers.

***

When Frank returned home, he soon had Claypit Hall in good shape. Not only did he work prodigiously hard himself but also it became apparent that with him, rather than under him, the paid employees seemed capable of a very improved performance. He was forever finding fresh ways of doing some of the more laborious and primitive tasks of the farm work of that day. His first harvest completely filled the stackyard and they won the cup at the Christmas fatstock show. Old Thomas did not think of paying his son a salary, but maybe the lad's stock of pigs increased somewhat. He was also allowed to fatten his own yard of bullocks.

Frank was encouraged in his livestock keeping by Harry Broyd, who by now had a connection with a successful London wholesale carcass butcher and a substantial guarantee at the bank. Frank's good 'eye' for stock developed and he was an expert judge of weight of all classes of livestock, a necessary qualification, especially with sheep. Of these there were numerous breeds all with a different length of fleece and deceptive in size and weight.

Livestock trade was always variable. The wholesale meat trade tended to be erratic and depended on the availability of grazing and roots. If keep was short, more animals would be slaughtered and force the wholesale price down. Pigs were notoriously 'muck or money'. Mrs. Sow was capable of producing a family of ten every six months, and if pigs were profitable, many more females would be bred from. If they were unprofitable, the breeding stock would be turned into sausage meat.

Harry developed a trade by supplying his customers with stock which would thrive. He well knew the value of being re-offered the finished article, be it lamb, hog or fat bullock. A satisfied customer would be most likely to stick to him.

***

Driving to market about that time, Old Thomas was again reflecting on his wife's continual injunction that he must 'do something' about Frank. Do something, but what? He had more or less given his milling business to Samuel. Old Thomas had had a setback years before over the bankrupt bakers. Claypit Hall, under Frank's management was growing a splendid crop, but it was the old man's sole asset. He had to provide for his old age and for his three unmarried daughters. There seemed little prospect of their getting married due to a dearth of farmers' sons or suitable spouses in the district. Young Jos, Old Thomas's wife's godson, excellent at all social occasions, often M.C. at a dance and certainly a very big talker, was a possibility. His father had a large farm, but was a slow payer of his milling account. Jos was a gambler and was always challenging his friends to toss for various stakes. Once at a dance he had challenged Frank to toss. Frank had refused. "You will never toss with me," Jos complained, "are you afraid to lose?"

"I am not afraid to lose. If you think I am, I will have one toss with you."

"Very well, we will toss for a case of port wine. You call."

"Heads."

"The devil! Heads it is. Now I will toss you for a case of whisky." "No thank you, Jos. You will remember I offered to have one toss with you. That is enough for me, thank you."

When the case of port arrived, it was tabooed by the family at the instigation ofFrank's mother, Joss's godmother, who was well aware of her godson's limited means. Not only was she godmother to the loser, but also she strongly disapproved of gambling of any sort. Frank was philosophical. Failing to share the first bottle with his family, he consoled himself with the fact that port improved with keeping. Keep it he did. On suitable occasions years later, it tasted very good, though Frank also disapproved of gambling, at least of gambling when he lost.

***

On the Corn Exchange Old Thomas was approached by Swallow-All Newman's cousin, a successful auctioneer and landagent, a relation by marriage to Thomas, who had been persuaded by him to buy his modern sideboard. Newman had wished to get rid of an unwanted wedding present in order to buy a Georgian model of that middle class status symbol.

"Thomas, I have a farm to let which will be just the thing for young Frank," said Newman, "our mutual second cousins are coming out of Wincey Farm. They wish to give up on Lady Day, are prepared to transfer the lease 'lock, stock and barrel': the cultivations to be carried out for the growing crop, horses, implements and stores to be paid for. The rent is stiffish for these times, but the farm is near and handy for you and I hear young Frank is a rare hard worker."

"I don't know about that," replied Old Thomas, "it is true my son is anxious to get started in a farm. You have not told me the sum required for the ingoing. It's bound to be a substantial amount."

"I have not yet arrived at a figure. All work done for the crop must be paid for, including last year's fallows. There are six months less time to wait till harvest can be realised than if you go in at Michaelmas. Maybe I could persuade our cousins to half the ingoing stand over for six months, if you would take it. You think it over and let me know next market day."

The Quaker, Joseph Smith, approached the stand and after the usual exchange of greetings, Old Thomas asked Joseph his opinion on the proposition of hiring Wincey Farm for Frank. Said Joseph: "A Lady Day entry is a very good thing if you are following a good farmer on good land. You have the benefit of half of what can be a good crop. I don't know the farm well. I always thought it a poorish place. I think they only got a small acreage of winter wheat sown last autumn. The family there are coming to the end of their financial tether. Some sort of cousins of yours aren't they? I always say, 'eat and drink with friends and relations, but do business with strangers."

In spite of this caution based on long experience, Frank could not be stopped. It was agreed he would continue to look after Claypit Hall for his father, and farm Wincey for himself. A down payment on the astronomical ingoing would be accepted and a substantial balance could be held over till Michaelmas.

Suitable arrangements were made with the bank and Frank took possession of his first farm on 25th March, 1893, when he was twenty-five years old.

IV

WINCEY

The land of Frank's new farm ran down to the boundary of Finchingfield. A dry early spring had enabled all the spring sowing to be completed before Lady Day. The cost of all this, of course, inflated the very heavy ingoing. Alas for Frank, the spring cultivations had been inadequate and the seed had been badly drilled. There ensued the drought of the century. Much of the seed sown before Lady Day lay ungerminated in the ground at harvest time. Frank's sparse first crop was cut with scythes. Appalled by the paucity of his stackyard at Michaelmas, Frank did a rapid calculation of his financial position. He owed twice as much as his total assets. The balance of his ingoing would have to wait. He had fallowed some of the worst of the fields of ungerminated seed. He had also made a sizeable stack of good hay. In spite of a lease forbidding its sale, Frank soon put it on offer. The drought had been universal and the hay crop very light. London's teeming thousands of horses had to be fed, and hay was at famine prices. A buyer, who seemed half a gipsy, called one afternoon. A deal was concluded by the dealer paying Frank two hundred and ten gold sovereigns for the hay. He stayed the night but got so drunk and aggressive that Frank went to bed with a loaded gun.

Soon after this, Harry Broyd called and Frank explained his predicament.

"What are you going to do?" enquired the young cattle dealer.

"I shall hold on till I bust," came the instant reply. "I fallowed some of the fields which failed, that makes two year's fallow for some of the land. I should get a good crop next year. Someone will have to trust me with some seed."

"I know nothing about your arable land troubles, but the livestock trade is in a bad way. There are no roots in the country and every sort of fodder is at famine prices. Every animal, be it pig, sheep or bullock, if it carries any flesh, is being killed as fodder is so short. In consequence there is such a glut of meat the price is on the floor. It is certain there will be a shortage of meat of all sorts next summer or my name is not Harry Broyd," said the instinctive dealer. "You let me send you some strong lambs, half bred Lincolns or the like; something tough! They can winter and half starve on weeds. Let me send you some empty sows. Pigs are always muck or money. They were muck before this drought. By the time the sows have produced and reared their litters, hogs will be short and worth good money. Your brother is a miller, he makes a tidy lot of wheat offal from his flour trade, he could trust you with some grub for your stock. I shan't want any money for the stock I send you, though I admit that knowing you have that two hundred sovereigns makes me easier in my mind because you could pay it you had to. You helped when I had my horse stolen. Let me help you now."

"Done," said Frank, and shook his friend's hand.

Fortunately, Claypit Hall, faithfully husbanded by Frank, carried a bountiful crop that year, proving some truth in the old adage that 'a good farmer never needs rain'. Old Thomas was in a better position to help his hasty son. Samuel more than came up to scratch with all that the mill could provide in the way of cattle food.

Two hundred strong-framed lambs, of the make and shape to exist on meagre fare, arrived at Wincey Farm. A half score of empty sows were also sent by the dealer. These were so thin Frank enquired if they were half-bred grey-hounds.

Soon after, Samuel was on the Corn Exchange when he was approached by a seedy individual who enquired if the miller could do with some cheap feeding stuff. The miller regarded the visitor to his stand with disfavour.

"What is the nature of the cheap feeding stuff you are offering?" he enquired.

"A cargo of lentils has arrived at the docks and it is infested with weevil. The importer has rejected the cargo and it lays on the quay. If it is not cleared by tomorrow it is to be loaded on to barges and taken out to sea and dumped overboard. I have cleared some of it at two pounds a ton. If you can do with any, that is all it will cost you over the rail charge, though I shall want ten shillings per ton commission."

Samuel listened to this tale with the hair rising on the back of his neck. He would rather have a man with the plague in his mill, than grain infested with weevil. But could Frank do with it?

"I am afraid I cannot buy weevil at any price," he replied. "It is just possible I might place some if I could see my customer."

"You do that and send me a telegram in the morning."

On his return from Market, Samuel immediately contacted his brother, "If you think you could do with these lentils, you must not store them or have them anywhere near your farmstead. You must sweep your waggons out and your men must brush their clothes. The sacks must be burnt as soon as emptied. Only a severe frost will kill weevil and if you get it in your barn it will take a long frost to get rid of it and you may have it for years."

A telegram was sent, and a few days later 12 tons of lentils arrived at Rayne Station. They were carted to the farm in three four-horse waggon loads then off-loaded into a long heap like a root clamp. Next they were thatched over to keep out the rain and an air tunnel was run up the entire length to 'let in the frost'.

Frank afterwards described these lentils as his 'widow's cruse'. They were carefully rationed together with bran (wheat husk) from the mill, to both the sheep and sows. Frank himself lived as near the bread line as he could that winter.

It was over at last, and the spring flush of grass coinciding with a shortage of meat caused livestock prices to rocket, just as Harry Broyd had foreseen. He bought the lambs back and handed Frank a cheque for £300 'for their keep'. The 'grey-hound' sows produced large litters which were sold in a 'flying' trade. Wincey carried a very promising crop after the year of failure. With some of the £300 Frank purchased one of the new 'self-binders' and cut his corn himself. He was not only saved, but found himself in the unbelievable position of commanding a large supply of profitable commodities.

V

FAINT HEART NEVER WON FAIR LADY

Frank lost no time in acquiring a big thoroughbred mare on which he could ride to hounds. He also bought a high sporting gig in which he could drive his new purchase to market. His next venture in the sporting line was not so fortunate. He acquired a second-hand penny-farthing bicycle. He did not grudge the considerable effort needed to propel it, he had more brute strength than most. How better could he use it than by 'keeping up with the Joneses'?

He had accepted an invitation to tennis one hot summer evening. On the penny-farthing he was able to carry his racquet, with some difficulty, but he had an enjoyable evening. The only drawback was that the party kept on longer than Frank had bargained for and the claret cup had been well laced with gin. After saying goodnight Frank found himself pedalling away homewards in the gathering dusk. "Confound it," he thought, "I ought to have been home before this to shut up my chickens. That old vixen from the Justices earth will be after them. Richardson told me he had a litter of cubs there."

Alas for Frank. He cut a corner on a fresh-tarred road in the village and his penny-farthing collapsed. His flannels were ruined, the bicycle broken and his leg badly bruised. He had to leave his crippled mount in the village and make his way home on 'Shanks's pony', in this case, somewhat lame.

Lame or not, he ran the last couple of hundred yards as he could hear the vixen at work on his pullets. He counted himself lucky to lose no more than a dozen.

Frank took his bicycle to the shop to be repaired.

"You ought to have something better than that old bone shaker. They are quite out of date," remarked the cycle engineer. "Why don't you invest in one of these Raleighs? They are the latest thing. They have these pneumatic tyres and even a lady can propel them. Take a look at this new one I have just got in especially for a lady."

Frank was shown how the tyres were inflated with an air

pump, and how the wheels ran on ball bearings. Remembering the exertion needed for the penny-farthing, he was somewhat incredulous about a lady being able to propel the machine.

"Who is the lady you are getting this for?" enquired Frank.

"I have ordered it specially for Miss Legerton."

Frank reflected, "Fanny Legerton: Winterflood's daughter: So the belle of Finchingfield is going to show herself off on a bicycle!"

Ladies had never yet been seen on a bicycle in this district, though the London papers were always reporting and, indeed, illustrating this latest female craze of doubtful propriety. The new machines were certainly expensive. Frank's old penny farthing had cost him a new pair of flannel trousers and twelve pullets. Fanny Legerton indeed! If she could have a new machine, could not Frank have the same? Maybe he would meet her when he was cycling? Maybe he would be going the same way? Maybe she would like an escort? People often fell off. Ladies would need picking up and perhaps helping on.

"You are quite right," Frank told the engineer. "My machine is perhaps not the latest thing. If you can repair it and give me what I gave you for it in part exchange for a new gentleman's Raleigh, you can order one for me."

"Leave it to me, Mr. Smith, I don't know if I can do that, but I will get as near as I can."

The new bicycle proved a stunner. With Frank's strength it went like the wind. It was however a bad investment in so far as meeting Fanny Legerton was concerned. Apparently she only appeared on her new machine in the mornings when Frank was at work. The appropriate lady's cycling costume was unsuitable for afternoon or evening wear. Frank's observation of this daring female was confined to the opportunity afforded by Sunday morning and evening services at church, and occasional meetings at social events.

The new machine did, however, open up new horizons. With its aid he was able to attend the balls at the Shire Hall. In those days of depression, much of the Essex land was looking for fresh farmers, and a substantial Scottish invasion into Essex agriculture took place. In the Shire Hall, Frank met the Scottish girls 'who could work all day and dance all night'. Doubtless he had a good look at these active and vivacious beauties, but somehow he could not forget the belle of his own village. Was there anything these Scottish girls could do that she could not do better? At the County Show had not her butter taken first prize? Had she not also won an award for dressed poultry? Was not her home baked bread only down graded because of the thickness of its crust? Could the crust of bread ever be too thick anyway? Did not these Scottish people breakfast on porridge and make scones of a puddingy nature? Frank preferred a breakfast of home-cured bacon or ham, and his father had always washed it down with a jug of home-brewed ale.

Fanny might be a forward Miss, but she was also surrounded by a formidable family of the venerable father, sagacious mother, 5 sons and 3 daughters. However, faint heart never won fair lady, and the family certainly did not daunt Frank.

The sons were as lighthearted as their father was serious. Frank soon learned that the old man was notorious for never taking more than one whisky during an evening's entertainment. He did sometimes receive a large one from a host who knew him, but when he finished his drink he always said 'goodnight' to his host. The younger generation visitors also learned that when the old man finished his drink at home he said 'goodnight' to his guests. It was 'turning out time'.

Frank was an early victim of the practical jokes which the brothers reserved for the swains of their sisters. Arriving for the evening with his new horse and high gig, he thought he might be cutting a suitable dash. After a pleasant evening, he unstabled his thoroughbred and put her in the gig, having first lighted the candle in each of his carriage lamps. The usual lengthy adieux were in this case cut extremely short as the highly bred horse showed signs of rearing on its hind legs with impatience to get home. Frank sprang up into the gig and they set off homewards at a furious pace. After a distance, Frank noticed one of his lamps had gone out, and then he noticed the other had also gone out. Curious! He had charged them with new candles not so long ago. Did the candles have a shorter burning life than he had calculated? In any case nothing could be done. His new horse could not be stopped before it reached the stable yard. It was not so dark that the illumination of a couple of candles made any great difference. Anyway, the purpose of the carriage lamps was to enable the vehicle to be seen rather than to aid the driver to see his way by their dim glow.

Frank reached home in record time without incident and was able to stable his horse in the dark, his mind all the time occupied with tender thoughts of the dark-haired Miss.

The threshing tackle arrived next morning and Frank was too fully occupied for the rest of the week to take any trips in his gig. When next he did, he examined his candle lamps. The candle was housed in a tube containing a jack-in-the-box spring. As fast as the wax burned down, the flame was pushed up to the correct level. The tube was fastened by a short screwing device: he discovered the tubes under his precious lamps were missing. He had no doubt that one of Fanny's brothers had given the tubes the necessary half turn to make them insecure, and the vibration of the fast pace of his mare had completed the trick. Frank never forgave the future brother-in-law who was responsible for this prank. He managed to obtain some more candle holders which fitted his lamps only by buying a very old pair of lamps with broken glass.

Another example of those young men's 'good will' took place on the occasion of a coursing meeting on their farms. One of the other sister's swains, Solly, attended. Maybe the fun of seeing a hare caught and killed by greyhounds would be some compensation for his lack of progress with the fair sex. This lack of progress was understandable. Solly was slow of speech and slower of movement, in fact, the complete 'slow coach'. The dark-haired, high-spirited tennis-playing and cycling girls bore with him with unfailing friendliness as he had grown up on the next-door farm and their mother was his godmother. Solly was pleasantly surprised when the brothers offered to mount him on a pony to view the coursing. The clay fields were in a most sticky condition and he was apt to lag behind at the best of times.

After a very successful day's coursing he returned to the farm. The horse's legs were plastered with clay and Solly also was very well-splashed with this sticky commodity.

"Take him in the lake and wash his legs," enjoined his young hosts.

Solly gladly complied while his hosts watched expectantly from the bank. Arrived in the middle of the lake, the pony proceeded to lie down and roll. During the process, Solly parted company with his mount. He walked out of the lake with water running out of the seat of his breeches and made the immortal enquiry from the appreciative audience: "What do you think of that now?"

What indeed! Solly's mount, as Fanny's brothers well knew, had an unfailing habit, as some horses do, of always lying down and rolling in the horse pond.

***

Frank's courtship proceeded at the necessarily steady pace of those times. A man had to be in a position to provide a suitable home for his 'intended', to say nothing of an established financial position sufficient for the not easily satisfied parents of the bride. Fanny's mother, Julia, was, before she married, one of the redoubtable Totman sisters, three heiresses. She determined that her priority in bringing up her children should be education, regardless of sex. She had therefore sent Fanny to one of the very first boarding schools for young ladies at Stamford. Frank was quite unperturbed by his blue-stocking belle, could he not recite by heart from *King Lear*? Did he not know *Othello* as if he were his brother? Was not *The Taming of The Shrew* his favourite play? On second thoughts, perhaps that would not be a good thing to mention.

The courtship was noticed by the Miss Bedalls - two formidable battleaxes who were the social arbiters of the district. Every newcomer to Finchingfield was ostracised till the Miss B's made known their approval. To them, Frank's thrusting business ways were deeply suspect. Business progress was the reverse of a social recommendation in an age when complete gentility depended mainly on not being compelled to work for a living, but to live entirely on a Private Income. Nor were Fanny's cycling exploits any recommendation to these of propriety, and certainly not her unladylike postures on the tennis court which were visible even from the road. And her companion's carefree but unladylike exclamations during the game quite properly shocked them. The battleaxes let fall the prediction that Fanny "Would ride in her carriage one day," a dictum which, to the pinnacle of society, was damning if reached by the process of trade, but which to those lower down in the social scale, was a recommendation.

The two Miss B's shared the services of an old gardener with the vicar. One day the vicar's daughter remarked to the gardener how surprised she was these two ladies of unquestionable taste and social position and possessed of a moderate competence, had remained unmarried. He replied; "Well Miss, it were like this here. Time they was young, them as would hev they, they wouldn't hev. Time they was older, them as they'd hev wouldn't hev they"'

***

One market day in May, Frank was introduced to a London estate agent, who was acting for the London owners of Jekyls Farm, Finchingfield, and was looking for a tenant. They needed someone capable of handling a tough proposition. The farm was virtually derelict and could be had on a long lease at a low rent. Frank agreed to have a look and was given an order to view. Mentioning the matter to his fiancée, he enquired if the farm had not at one time belonged to some of her relatives.

"Indeed yes", replied Fanny, "but it was always very unlucky for them."

This was a Finchingfield tale Frank had not heard.

Jekyls never did Fanny's second cousin, Totman, any good. In the first place his daughter unfortunately engaged her affections to an extremely doubtful army Captain during some military manœuvres around there. The Totmans would have none of him, and the couple arranged to elope. A tryst was arranged at midnight, at the end of the avenue of trees which led up to the farm. After lights out the girl affected her escape, undiscovered, through the scullery window. The Captain was to fetch her with a coach hired from Braintree, where, of course, there was a railway station. A tremendous thunderstorm broke over the district. When the Captain in his coach was passing Abbots Hall Park, a tree was struck by lightning just in front of the horses.

They bolted. Turned the coach over. It lost a wheel. The Captain sustained a broken arm. The girl endured the night of terror beneath the avenue trees, waiting in vain for her lover. At first light of dawn she returned to the house soaked to the skin. Her re-entry via the scullery window was accomplished undiscovered, but tell-tale pools of water from her soaking garments were noticed in the morning and the story was wrung from her.

Totman had been a good hard-working farmer. He owned but two thirds of Jekyls Farm, the remaining third having been left in a will to a distant branch of the family. He wished to buy out the third share and consulted lawyer Cutts on how to proceed.

"You make an offer and I will go and see the owners of the third share in London. I will try and arrange a deal if you pay me a commission," directed Cutts.

"Very well," replied Totman, "I will give four thousand pounds for the third share."

"Is that enough? Would you take twice that amount for your shares?"

"It is a fair price and I would take twice the amount for my two-thirds."

The lawyer wrote a few lines on a sheet of paper and asked Totman to sign, which he did, without reading it. Cutts proceeded to London and found the co-owner to be a prosperous brewer. Sounding him on the project of Jekyls Farm, Cutts discovered the brewer was more interested in buying than selling. Scenting a double commission on the sale of two thirds, rather than the purchase of one third. Cutts enquired if his client would be willing to pay eight thousand pounds for the two-thirds? The brewer consented and signed a sheet of paper on which Cutts had written a few lines. Cutts then returned home and informed Totman that he had sold his two thirds to the brewer.

"You may think so, but you will find your mistake," shouted the infuriated Totman, "I instructed you to buy, not to sell."

"Oh no. You offered four thousand pounds to buy, or eight thousand pounds to sell. You signed an offer to that effect."

Totman had indeed signed, without reading the offer, but he stood his ground. There ensued a legal action. A signed offer was deemed to be a binding contract, and Totman lost.

One day later on, Winterflood Legerton met the Sheriff of Essex, who was proceeding to Jekyls to evict Totman. On learning this, Legerton persuaded the sheriff to come to his house and stay the night in order that Winterflood could reason with his relative by marriage. This he did, and on Totman giving a signed undertaking to vacate, for which Winterflood had to stand surety, the eviction was called off. It broke Totman's heart and he took his family off to New Zealand.

One afternoon late in November Cutts visited Winterflood in his carriage with some papers for him to sign. Cutts was asked to tea, during which one of the pullets 'went to roost' on the axle of his carriage. It stuck to its roost and not only travelled to Cutts's home, but laid an egg the next morning. He scrounged some food for the pullet and made a great fuss of it. He claimed its eggs were the best he'd tasted; ' A taste for ill-gotten gains.', so the tale went.

Fanny was well versed in local gossip. She was able to keep Frank well informed... "It would appear Jekyls has not done the London brewers much good," she told him, "they tried to keep a thoroughbred stud there, filled in some draining ditches to make a training gallop, installed a small time trainer as manager and left things to him. He gambled away everything on the farm that could be cashed. Then his wife died and her people had to send money for her funeral expenses. When it came he went to Newmarket and gambled it away. Her folks had to pay again to bury their daughter. He has now disappeared, the farm is derelict and there are a few weedy colts left with one man in charge."

***

Frank inspected the farm. The lease was prepared and signed. Later, in the Corn Exchange, he engaged a steam tackle to bring the derelict land into cultivation. On 10th June, 1898, the 'Injins' as Finchingfield called them, arrived. These consisted of two huge steam engines equipped with a large winding drum of steel cable with which they hauled a massive cultivator to and fro across the fields. Working long hours and blessed with dry weather, they transformed the weed-choked farm to clean cultivated land in weeks. A short fallow was long enough and Frank grew a heavy crop of wheat the following year.

Frank's home was Wincey's mean little farmhouse. He knew very well it was an unsuitable abode for his important fiancée, the daughter of Winterflood and Julia Totman. The lease was running out. His early, near-disastrous, experience had not endeared him to the place. A substantial farm with a substantial house, called Petches, not far from Jekyls, became vacant. He gave up Wincey and hired it. At last he could celebrate his nuptials in time to move in at Michaelmas.

'What did you think of that, now?'

VI

PETCHES

Alas for Frank, the land on the new farm was not so productive as he had hoped, though it carried a flock of ewes well. A small stream bordered the farm in which were some nice-ish trout. The district road surveyor was a keen angler and made friends with Frank in order to cast an occasional lure in the small stream. He arrived one Saturday to find the river in spate and unfishable. He needed no pressing to take tea with the new bride.

"Frank," he announced, "I have a business proposition for you to consider. I need a large quantity of stone to repair the roads around here. My predecessor seems to have properly let them go and I have had special instructions from the council to carry out an extensive programme of renewal. We first of all put down a layer of sifted stone, level it and break the largest flints with a stone hammer. We then put down a layer of the siftings or hoggin, wet it from a water cart and roll it well with a steam roller. Where I am going to repair a road I have to have sufficient stone and siftings dumped on the greensward beforehand. Barker's pit is worked out, he and his men are torn out, I am looking for a fresh supplier. If you could get the gravel dug, sifted and carted to where I want, I could pay a fair price. You have that little old gravel pit on the way to the river. It looks as though it might be pretty good stuff and contain some clean stone. Why don't you have a try at the job when you are not busy on the land. I can then see what sort of stuff the pit will yield and, if suitable, give you a firm order for a large quantity".

So began a business, developed by Frank into a profitable sideline. It was hard work for his men. They first of all dug and removed the 'overburden', throwing it across the excavated pit leaving a hole about 4 feet into the face of the vein of gravel, which was then loosened with a pickaxe and one man threw the loosened gravel up to his mate who caught the shovelful on a round sieve, held in readiness over a barrow. He then shook the sieve over the barrow; the smaller stones and sand fell through. The large stones he cast into another barrow. When the barrows were full, they were pushed along a heavy duck-board and the contents built into symmetrical heaps a yard high. The men were paid on piecework and made about 50% over their weekly rate: a useful addition to their meagre wages in winter, when extra money was scarce. It enabled Frank to keep more men, and, more important, more horses. The sifted stone was shovelled into tumbrels of 1½ tons capacity. These were then hauled by two horses up to five miles to where they were required.

A larger team of horses and men on the farm thus became economic, a great help to better cultivations and a quicker harvest. Frank used to buy and break-in two colts every year. A reputable horse dealer supplied him with the type of colt which when fully trained Frank could sell for a town horse to join the thousands at work in London. All prices for these activities were low, but all carried a small margin of profit.

One day, one of the gravel diggers, having by hard work earned some surplus cash, celebrated by having too much beer. In his inebriated state he demanded the whole heap of stones be measured up at once and the balance due to him paid, as he was 'off to a job in Yorkshire'. Young men were recruited from Essex for Yorkshire farms. There they were lodged, fed, and worked for a yearly contract. It was often a good move for an Essex lad who might be one of a family of ten, living in a small ill-ventilated cottage, getting barely enough food. In Yorkshire there were potatoes and milk *ad lib*, with a generous supply of home killed pork. Some weedy lads from Finchingfield had returned as strong young men after three or four years in the 'wilds of the North'. The same practice obtained in Scotland. There, however, the comfort of the worker was looked after by a standard form of agreement whereby the employer agreed not to serve salmon as a main meal more than four times per week.

***

Fanny produced two daughters and then a son. On the day of the son's birth, Harry Broyd sent Frank a hundred ewe lambs. When they were counted, the tally was a hundred and one. Harry, when he heard suggested the one over should go to the 'heir'. This was accepted joyfully and was the means whereby Ben entered the farming business at one day old.

Fanny was assisted in the house by plenty of domestic help. She managed all the arduous routine of a farmhouse with easy expertise. Monday was washing day. Then Polly would appear at 8 a.m. from Finchingfield, a mile away. Polly had 'made a mistake' in her youth, her illegitimate daughter was reared elsewhere, she lived in single loneliness, ostracised to some degree by the village. On arrival at Petches, she would expect the copper to be full of rainwater and heated by the kitchen boy to near boiling point. She would then do the family wash in the morning. This entailed washing the linen in zinc baths by hand, transferring it to the copper and boiling it, removing the scalding mass to rinsing water, putting it 'through the blue', sometimes starching it, mangling it with a hand 'wringer', and pegging it on the line to dry. When dry, it would be brought in, damped down and folded ready for ironing. Polly would do some of the ironing in the afternoon before returning home in the evening. She combined competent industry with an exceedingly sharp tongue if things were not just right! On one occasion she received a sharpish answer from a stockman to whom she complained when his cattle strayed into the farmhouse garden where her linen was drying. Her rejoinder was long remembered, "I ain't going to be trud (trodden) on'."

Tuesday was churning day, when the week's cream from daily skimming of the milk pans was made into butter. In warm weather this necessitated rising in the cool of dawn in order that the butter would not 'come soft'. Butter-making was not an exact process. The cream was poured into a barrel-shaped end-over-end churn, which was turned by hand until the butter 'came'. It was necessary for the temperature of the cream to be 60°F., therefore cold or hot water sometimes had to be added to make the butter 'come'. The butter-milk was drawn off, the butter rinsed in cold water, soaked in brine according to taste, pressed with a butter worker, and made up into pats with wooden 'butter hands' previously scalded and kept in cold water. Sometimes the butter was a long time coming, as Ben grew to boyhood he was often put to turning the churn in order to keep him out of mischief.

Wednesday was 'market day'. Fanny had regular customers

in Braintree for her butter and eggs. She rode with Frank in the gig when the exigencies of the family permitted, she learnt the truth of the country proverb:

When you have one you can run;
When you have two you can goo;
When you have three, you must bide where you be.

As the family grew older they were sometimes taken on the weekly marketing expedition. Now and then they were left at the 'White House' with Fanny's childless great aunt whilst Fanny did the household shopping. On a memorable occasion young Ben was more than usually naughty. At lunch he asked for a second helping of 'pudden'.

"You must say 'pudding," remonstrated the prim old lady.

"Pudden!" Ben insisted. He seized an apple dumpling and ran off into the garden shouting "pudden, pudden, pudden."

When Fanny returned to collect her brood, she received the devastating adieu: "Good-bye, Fanny, I am so sorry you cannot control your children."

Thursday would be 'cleaning or pickling' day in the morning, and visiting day in the afternoon. Jams and pickles were all home made. Once a year a pig was killed which necessitated all the paraphernalia of boiling up brawn, mincing for sausages, lard rendering etc. The pig was always killed 'when the moon was on the make'. The same process carried out when the moon was on the wane was apparently fatal!

Friday was 'baking day'. Fanny early learned that the way to Frank's heart was through a crusty home-baked cottage loaf. Every farmhouse in those days was equipped with a bread oven, a domed brick structure built into a chimney, heated with faggots of wood which were drawn out when the oven was near white hot and the bread put in.

Saturday would be 'general clearing up day'. Fanny would get up at 5 a.m., as she did every day except Sunday, and begin by cleaning the lamps.

Sunday was strictly observed as the Sabbath. The family always attended church in the morning and sometimes in the afternoon, the evening was spent visiting or entertaining neighbours and relatives.

The visit to Church, more than a mile distant, was accomplished by walking if at all possible. When the weather was bad, a pony and governess cart was provided. In that case, an early start was imperative as the pony had to be stabled at the 'Lion', kept by the formidable Mr. Tucker. As he was one of the sidesmen in church it would have been a crime of the first order to make him late or even give him insufficient time to don his silk topper and frock coat after assisting in tying up the pony in the inn stable. No one ever spoke of Mr. Tucker without the Mr. He had long served as butler in one of the stately homes and had acquired the dignity of that responsible position. For some reason unknown he had gone prematurely bald. He had, in fact, not a single hair on his head. When his old master died, Mr. Tucker had felt unable to take an appointment with the young heir who had for years cracked poor jokes on the condition of the butler's pate. Mr. Tucker had then left their service and taken the 'Lion', bringing with him the dignity and taste of his long appointment. It was impossible to get drunk at the 'Lion' and the conversation was usually on the doings of the 'county' with a capital 'C', a subject of inexhaustible interest and one on which mine host always seemed extensively informed.

Before her marriage, Fanny's family had always made the journey to church by wagonette from their distant farm. It was church in the morning, but in the afternoon, worship was practised in the chapel. The Totmans had been prominent non-conformists and not only that, having independent means, Julia, Mrs. Legerton, had financial backing for her dissention. Finchingfield described the curious alternation of divine worship as 'dodging the Devil both ways'.

***

Fanny never complained of her demanding routine and, if she sometimes tired, it was due to her natural devotion to her family. She was assisted by willing helpers, her resident domestic help found service in the roomy farmhouse, with its plain but generous fare, infinitely preferable to the crowded and confined life of large families in small cottages where food would always be limited if not scarce.

A horseman's widow would come and do the sewing and

mending for the family. Her greatest reward would be a square meal with company and gossip. Her happy nature ensured a welcome, her sentiments were revealed by a remark made when she was preparing a layette for another regular arrival, "And whiles I works I stitches in the love."

A boy on the farm would be 'kitchen boy' and 'boots' as required. He would heat the copper and bread oven, carry the copious fuel for the fires inside. Money was scarce even for low priced coal. The previous tenant of Petches was reputed to have bought 2 tons of coal yearly for the princely sum of £2. This would be carted from Braintree station in a farm waggon. The farmer then buried the coal under a stack of firewood, thus forcing his wife to consume large quantities of firewood which cost nothing in cash, in order to uncover the purchased coal.

Fanny usually had an able lieutenant in the form of a mother's help or a nursery governess who was supposed to instruct and discipline the growing infants.

One busy morning during spring cultivations, Frank came in to a late breakfast to be informed the governess was going home for a short break and had to be taken to catch the train. While he finished his meal, his thoroughbred was harnessed to his gig and Frank and the governess set off at a spanking pace. He used to boast he could drive this mare with two strands of knitting wool, he always carried a whip but never hit her except once. It happened thus. On the way to the station with the governess, they came upon a team of roadmen repairing the road, work which necessitated the use of a wheelbarrow which was standing at the side of the road. The highly bred and, perhaps, highly fed horse refused to pass this lowly contraption. Frank, an expert horsemaster if ever there was one, got down from the driving seat and took the mare by the bridle to lead her past the fearsome object. It was wholly in vain. The mare was as immovable as a rock. "Confound the mare," thought Frank, "confound the governess; confound the train; confound all females! I will teach this one a lesson." With the butt end of the whip he struck the mare a heavy blow along her ribs. Her response was to lie down in the road in silent rebuke.

For a horse to go down in shafts was a very serious thing. In struggling to get up, harness was frequently broken and often the shafts to the gig to which the horse was harnessed were broken as well. In this case the mare was got safely to her feet with harness undamaged and Frank recovered his senses. The offending wheelbarrow was pushed into a field, out of sight, Frank climbed back into the driving seat. Off they went and the train was caught.

The gallant mare was to lay down in shafts once more. A couple of years later, whilst trotting in the gig at a brisk pace, she suddenly stopped and lay down in the road. In this case her heart had stopped. Such was the regard which Frank had for her, he had her hoof mounted in silver and it is treasured to this day.

The activities of Frank's eldest boy, Ben, needed constant supervision. One day he was missing. The house and homestead were searched without result. A large field of corn was being cut by a corn binder nearby and the search extended to this field. The binder had commenced on the outside of the field and, by going round and round, reduced the uncut corn by a width of six feet each revolution. The machine was drawn by a team of three horses. The driver had to drive and steer the horses, make constant adjustments to the complicated machine, and see the sheaves were all tied. On this occasion, when the machine came round to meet the searchers, it was discovered the three year old Ben was asleep on the driver's lap. More serious was an attempt to play truant from the nursery by hiding in a field of six feet high maize which was grown for fodder.

Other children could also be a menace. Young Green tried an experimental cigarette behind two of Frank's cornstacks, standing quarter of a mile from the farmstead. Result: stacks engulfed in flames. The fire brigade, led by the redoubtable Sam Turner, the blacksmith, member of Finchingfield cricket team, the only man strong enough to hit the ball into the pond, was sent for. The horse to draw the fire engine was stabled further from it than the fire. The harness had been taken to pieces to clean and had to be assembled before the appliance could move. In due course, at 5 miles per hour, the speed of the horse, the machine arrived.

The fire engine was a hand pump worked by a team of ten men. It had two levers, rather like parallel bars, one on either side. Five men pushed one bar down for one stroke of the pump which elevated the opposite bar, and the process was repeated by the other half of the team. With strong and willing firemen working in relays, the engine was capable of delivering a considerable jet of water. When the team inevitably tired or drank too much beer 'it didn't pump ner faster than an old cow piddling', according to the village.

The captain took one look at Frank's fire, sent back to the village for 9 gallons of beer and sent to the farm for a water-cart full of water. In those days every farm was equipped with a tank on wheels to give water for the steam engine at threshing times and to wet the straw for thatching the corn stacks. In this case the firemen applied the load of water to the fire and then sat in the horse-van which had brought them to the scene of the fire and drank the nine gallons of beer. By the time they had finished, the fire had burnt itself out and they were able to return to Finchingfield.

Frank got into trouble with his insurance claim. The high-powered inspector who came along complained Frank was under-insured and bullied him into increasing his cover all round.

***

Petches Farm was endemic to 'twitch', a perennial weed with a creeping root. Turnips and trefoil were grown as cleaning crops. After being grazed off by sheep, the field would be thoroughly cultivated, the twitch harrowed into heaps, and burnt. As this burning sometimes took place during harvest when the farm staff were more gainfully employed, Frank himself assisted, accompanied by his five year old Ben, who found the making of bonfires to be great fun.

Petches had two stackyards. On one side were the haystacks handy for the stables and stockyards. The farmstead was centred round a huge thatched barn, at the back of this the men were building cornstacks in the second stackyard, convenient for the threshing machine. The day after helping with the twitch bonfires, Ben had the happy idea of tidying up the hay stackyard. He raked the loose straw into a large heap. When no-one was about, aided by his sister Jane, he climbed on a chair and lifted a box of matches from the high shelf in the kitchen. Ben lighted the heap of straw. In an instant the burning straw ignited a haystack. Sparks flew in all directions, fell on the thatch of the huge barn, and ignited the shavings made by a hurdle maker working in a neighbouring shed.

Frank was absent at Jekyls. A horseman galloped off on a hunter to summon him, and the Finchingfield fire brigade. Frank was reported as taking the corner leading from Jekyls on one wheel when returning home. He arrived at Petches at the same time as the fire brigade, just in time to see the roof of the thatched barn collapse in a sheet of flame. At once he organised the hanging of a stack sheet on the wall of the farmhouse and directed the feeble jet of water from the fire engine to the preservation of his home. The fire moved, and the cornstacks ignited. Stack sheets were hung and wetted on cornstacks to prevent the fire spreading. The farmhouse and some cornstacks were saved. The rest was burned flat. Frank somehow managed to reject the advice to horsewhip his 5 year old son.

The redeeming feature of the whole sorry business for Frank, was an interview with the same insurance inspector who had bullied him into inflating his insurance cover. Or maybe it was the opportunity to eat baked apples for his tea, picked ready-baked from a tree which had grown at the rear of the incinerated stables. Be that as it may, the substantial insurance claim for his hay, implements and stacks was put on deposit. Insurance for the barn and stables was the business of the landlord. To him things appeared very different. He rebuilt the stables, but in place of the huge thatched barn, a status symbol in the farming fraternity of that day, there appeared a corrugated iron monstrosity bodged up by a local builder.

VII

THE SQUIRES

The Squire of Finchingfield was a natural horseman and a nailing rider, he was also a dead shot. Being an expert in these two most important things in his life, and a social leader of the county, he assumed a fatal pose of business expert when business had to be done. Apart from the undoubted vulgarity of anything approaching 'trade', the Squire was notorious for never listening to any advice except his own. He had difficulty in making up his mind. When he did arrive at a business decision, it was invariably the wrong one. He had begun a business career by marrying the co-heiress of a successful London brewer and was made a director of the brewery on the strength of his wife's shares. For a time the brewery continued under the impetus of its late founder. The country was, however, going through a time of severe depression and the brewery was hit by severe competition and made some heavy losses. The Squire lost his nerve and sold his wife's shares for a pittance. He resigned his directorship amid gossip of 'rats leaving a sinking ship'.

A general meeting of shareholders of the brewery was held, and drastic re-organisation agreed upon, which included 'marking down the company's capital'. A new manager was appointed. Since that day the brewery has never looked back and grew to one of the national giants.

Inevitably, the Squire had a poor agent and poorish tenants on his large estate. Frank once undertook the direction of the Home Farm, but not for long. A substantial acreage of clover was then grown on farms in the district for rotational purposes. Clover was a fine preparation for a wheat crop. A leguminous plant, it had the gift of absorbing and fixing in the soil nitrogen from the atmosphere. Grown at intervals of eight years to avoid 'clover sickness' (a fungus disease which was endemic), it was first cut for hay early in June, the second growth or aftermath was either an attempted seed crop or fed to sheep. Clover was difficult stuff to cure when cut for hay. After cutting, it would be turned to speed up the drying, built into heaps about four feet wide and four feet high, locally called 'cocking'. Hay 'in the cock' would continue to dry out, but if a storm of rain fell, well made cocks were reasonably weather proof.

In that year Frank had a large field of clover hay cut on his own farm, also on the Home Farm for the Squire. In good weather the hay was turned, but as Frank said, "the confounded barometer was falling." Therefore he called up every available man to cock his own hay, and rushed off to do the same for the Squire. It was the Friday before Whit Monday and the men on both farms were given orders to finish cocking the hay before they left, even if it meant going home in the dark.

At lunch the Squire's wife reminded her husband the village fête was to take place in their grounds on the Monday and the place must be tidied up for the occasion. Accordingly the squad of haymakers was withdrawn from the hay-field for the non-productive preparations for festivity. The Squire's hay remained uncocked. It rained all day on Whit Monday, the fête was washed out, the hay completely spoiled and, soon after, Home Farm was without a manager.

***

Twelve miles distant, just the other side of Braintree was a bird of a different feather, the Squire of Stisted. A successful industrialist, he purchased the Stisted Estate with its three thousand acres and imposing mansion with the intention of promoting himself socially. He did not find the experience either successful or enjoyable. An aged retainer who 'went with the estate' was once asked why the industrialist did not stay longer at Stisted.

"It was like this here," explained the ancient philosopher, "when he come there, he were the Squire sure enough, but the other Squires, they wouldn't come nigh him. Then he bought a carriage and pair what had belonged to the Prince of Wales. He used to drive them to Braintree three times a week. That never made no difference. Then his wife died, and he took up with a housemaid and she got big. That wouldn't have been so bad, but he took and married her. After that, them what thought they was as good as he, wouldn't come nigh him, so he got fed up and he sold out and went back to Birmingham."

The retreat of this amateur gentleman was, however, ensured in quite a different way. A group of near-Squires were wont to foregather in each other's homes on a Sunday afternoon for a port drinking session. They were each possessed of an extensive cellar of wine of the finest vintages and considered themselves to be expert judges of wine when competence in that field was a social achievement. The port drinking sessions took the form of minute observation of the depth of colour of the port provided by the host and much 'bouqueting' and leisurely tasting at successive homes of this exclusive clique. The merits or otherwise of the wine were subject to informed and lengthy discussion and comparison by these connoisseurs.

The group thought they might as well be neighbourly to the new Squire and sent him an invitation which he accepted. On that occasion the host produced a decanter of his most famous vintage. After pouring a glass for each of his guests he asked the new Squire, "how would you describe this wine?" Alas for the new boy: Without a glance at its colour, without wafting the bouquet towards his rather snub nose, he took a generous swig and replied with confidence, "I should describe it as port." Port indeed! It was Cockburns '87, for fifteen years matured amid the cobwebs of the host's cellar and reverently decanted so as not to 'break the crust'. Port indeed! Never was social damnation self pronounced with such fatal clarity. The Squire was never asked to a port drinking session again, nor indeed anywhere else, for the story got around far and wide.

***

The best-known Squire in the Braintree area was Samuel Courtauld, who, by successful paternalism, was regarded with affection and respect by the multitude he employed in a very successful and lucrative business. His family factories were busily employed producing funeral crêpe. When families of ten or a dozen were common, death was a frequent visitor. When this occurred, all the females of the family had to turn out in voluminous black costumes made from Courtaulds black silk crêpe.

Courtauld purchased a large mansion and estate within reasonable distance of his three factories. To these he was driven

'What, did you leave the old b—r behind?'

each morning in his carriage and pair by his cockaded coachman sitting high on the driver's box in front of the enclosed coach. Courtauld invariably stayed a short time at his first factory before going on to the second. The horses were left harnessed to the carriage and tied up by their halters. While the Squire dealt with his post, the coachman was able to cross the road to the 'Black Boy' and enjoy the first pint of the day. Once, when Courtauld arrived at his office he discovered he had left his Gladstone (briefcase) at home. He hurried to his waiting carriage and horses and called for his coachman. In vain! His voice could not carry to the comfortable parlour of the 'Black Boy' where his unworried henchman was sipping a pint of 'mild and old'. Courtauld forthwith climbed on to the box and by plying the whip was soon proceeding up his own carriage drive. The footman, hearing the clipclop of the horse's hooves, rushed to the carriage entrance in time to open the door of the vehicle as it stopped. Intent on his prime duty, the footman did not bother to look up at the high box from which Courtauld was considering the best means of descent. Opening the door, perceiving the carriage to be empty the footman enquired of the supposed coachman, "What? Did you leave the old b - - r behind?"

***

The Squires seldom condescended to visit the Corn Exchange where their affairs were regularly discussed in minute detail by accomplished gossips. Probably no one was followed with keener interest, no scandal was more appreciated than that attached to the Countess. She was possessed of vast and fertile estates and an income of £30,000 per annum at a time when a farm worker's wages were twelve shillings per week. She was also exceptionally beautiful. The hunt adored her and were never tired of describing her at 'the most beautiful woman on a horse' or 'the most beautiful horsewoman'. Indeed she had a wonderful 'seat' and was always superbly mounted. Being an accomplished horsewoman, she rarely required assistance. Hunting is however prone to mischance, and once when negotiating a blind ditch, she parted company from her mount. A point-to-point rider caught her horse and gave her a leg up. Though he lost his own horse in doing so and missed the rest of the hunt, he cared not a jot.

Every minute of the hour he had spent in catching his own mount he considered an honour in the service of the famous Diana.

The Corn Exchange were not in the least surprised to learn that the Countess was being sought after by a royal Prince. This eminent personage seemed, as they said, to 'know his onions', or at least to have read his history. Instead of keeping a fabulously expensive mistress, he hit on a successful plan, 'making war support war'. Not only did he get his mistress to entertain himself and his retinue at her country house while he enjoyed her favours, but also saw to it that she was regularly invited to other stately homes where royal entertainment was the highest ambition of the owners. Amours thus cost him nothing.

When the Countess had a special railway station built on her estate for the convenience of her royal lover, she was thought by the countryside to be pushing her mistressing a bit too far, even if the station was constructed at the railway company's expense.

It became known that a royal coolness had developed. Some said it was due to the Countess giving birth to a child after a long period of infertility. One man, neither husband nor Prince, was reported to be furious because the child was not attributed to him. The Countess had the mansion refurnished and even had 'new bathrooms with solid silver taps' fitted for the comfort of her royal visitor. Alas, 'for reasons of state' he became respectable, or so it was thought by some. He never again travelled to the special station, nor visited the Countess, nor had a dip in the bath fitted with silver taps.

According to Mr. Tucker of 'The Lion', who had it from the footman employed by the Countess, the reason was something quite different. It became apparent that the Prince was becoming impotent, a condition aggravated by the advancing age of his long enjoyed mistress. He was thus compelled to seek his comfort with more juvenile nymphs.

Apart from the old adage that 'Hell hath no fury like a woman scorned', it transpired the Countess had spent her whole astronomic fortune on the prevailing style of 'mistressing' a Royal lover. More serious was the omission of the Countess from the invitation lists of the great houses. The green-eyed cats of society were no better or worse than in any other age, they exalted in their revenge on the once beautiful, imperious and sought-after favourite, with as little remorse as a pack of hunting wolves. Nor could her once admiring hunt defend her, for she adopted the Fabian creed and became an 'anti-bloodsports'.

She had not only spent every penny of her inheritance, but she was heavily in debt, had turned socialist and at one time offered the gift of her home for a socialist college, not accepted on account of the debt secured on it.

It is not to be thought the Countess worried as much about her debts as one might imagine. Furthermore, if any trader was a pal of her agent, as was the builder who fixed the solid silver taps, he would get paid if the agent said he would.

A Mr Stratton had purchased a partnership in a coal and builder's merchants business in Braintree and had a stand on the Corn Exchange. Before he had a chance to learn the oddities of the district, his new partner asked if he would call on the Countess, whose considerable coal account had remained unpaid for three years. To this he readily agreed.

Now Mr. Stratton was a very handsome man, blessed with a pleasant and engaging manner which he took pains to cultivate. In addition he possessed one of the first motor cars in the district. He drove over to the mansion in this fearsome contraption and pulled up under the stately carriage porch. He then removed his ankle-length driving coat, revealing a spotless morning suit beneath. For his peaked cap and goggles, he substituted an undeniable topper. The watching footman received him suitably at the imposing front door. Relieving the caller of the glossy topper and gloves and accepting Mr. Stratton's card, the flunkey ushered him into her Ladyship's boudoir. There the famous Countess, with an eye for a handsome man, received him graciously. After a suitable interval the caller attempted to work up to the purpose of his visit. As soon as the Countess grasped this, she engaged Mr Stratton in animated and non-stop conversation: "Was not the state of the roads a scandal? Was not the standard of teaching in elementary schools deplorable? Was it not time something was done about unmarried mothers?"

Mr. Stratton had, perforce, to agree and when he had managed to 'get a word in edgeways' the Countess suggested that, if they were to talk business, they could do it much more pleasantly over a drink. "Would Mr. Stratton take a glass of brandy?" Mr. Stratton would. "Would you give me your arm?" Mr. Stratton certainly would.

As they proceeded out of the boudoir to the back of the hall, Mr. Stratton reflected that, not so very long since, the ruler of the greatest Empire in the world's history had been glad to escort the Countess perhaps to this very spot. He was led to a well stocked bar where the butler was ordered to "pour Mr. Stratton a Napoleon." The Countess personally handed the glass to her guest and then asked to be excused for a moment.

Stratton was sipping his drink in a leisurely manner and awaiting her Ladyship's return, when a tall stranger joined him. "Mornin', Charles," the newcomer addressed the butler with great familiarity, "you can pour me a brandy. What do you know for the Derby? Lemberg won the Guineas easy enough but he is not bred to stay. That Elfin filly for the Oaks is a different cup of tea. Goes back to Cellini on both sides."

Stratton thought the strtanger was a member of the family. When he had finished his drink the Countess had still not returned. He therefore informed the butler he had some business to complete with her Ladyship. "If you will excuse me a moment I will inform her," replied that stately personage.

As he disappeared down the corridor, the newcomer turned to Stratton with the devastating remark "You are here after money, aren't you?" Much embarrassed, Stratton did confess to having an account to discuss with the noble Countess. "Well," averred the stranger, "you won't see her again today. Have another brandy. Let me fill your glass and have one of these Havanas. They are the best obtainable in London. I ought to know. My firm supply the booze and bacca for this place. I get sent down every month to collect some money. I never get any, but I always enjoy my visit from the time I arrive at the Royal station till I get back."

Stratton sipped his drink and puffed away at the fine cigar. The butler soon returned with the information that her ladyship was indisposed and wished to be excused. Stratton was able to make the journey home philosophically. The cigar was too good to hurry and the Countess's brandy certainly seemed to straighten the corners. He did not repeat the visit, but his firm was eventually paid. One of the men friends of the Countess 'managed' her debts for years and enabled her to die solvent.

***

Mr. Smoothy's most important case concerned the Squire of the huge Marks Hall estate, a stately Tudor mansion and 3,000 acres of surrounding farms. This was worth £9,000 a year when handed to the Squire by trustees when he became of age. With the aid of extravagant brothers, he had so far reduced this in twenty years that he had to raise a mortgage to pay one of his brother's debts of £12,000. He caught a chill which developed into pneumonia. A month before he had stood godfather to a distant relative. Calling Mr. Smoothy to his bedside, he dictated a new will. Having no family, he left the estate to his wife in trust for the month old godson and then died. The will was contested and the estate put in Chancery. So commenced a widespread and pitiless legal harvest. After a lengthy hearing, a partial settlement was agreed whereby the widow paid out the manorial rights which according to feudal law the Squire's brothers automatically inherited. This enabled the widow to maintain possession of the estate, but the Chancery case went on for fourteen years. The widow rebuilt the private church, but such was the agricultural depression that when she died, after twenty five years widowhood, the Court of Chancery seized the estate and sold everything to 'disperse the encumbrances', including their astronomical legal fees. When this had been done, the heir was found serving as a waiter in a London pub and told there was not one shilling of his inheritance left for him. That was the end for those Squires of Marks Hall.

VIII

HIS REVERENCE

Round about 1910, Frank received a visit from the jovial vicar of Finchingfield bringing an invitation to his annual 'Tithe Dinner' at the Vicarage, a sumptuous feast prepared for the farmers of the parish. This was followed by halfpenny nap, at which the vicar always won, and whisky, of which the vicar had a full share, until the small hours. Jimmy Oldfield, who had by now recovered from his devastating honeymoon in Margate and was churchwarden, was a regular guest. As his wife would not allow him to play cards for money, his part of the evening's entertainment was to shuffle the pack and replenish the whisky glasses. The vicar willingly trusted this part of his hospitality to his churchwarden. He said the warden could make the bottle last much longer than could the host.

The vicar was a red haired bachelor of around sixty and inclined to stammer when excited, which was often. Son of a noble family, he had purchased the rich 'living' of Finchingfield when it had been sold, at a time when the Squire could not raise the wind to buy it. The Squire was naturally jealous of the holy newcomer who owed him no homage. The vicar was also well qualified both financially and intellectually to be a social leader of the village. Why, he even gave a 'tithe dinner' to the Squire's tenants, who paid no tithe, but never entertained the Squire, who paid most of it The vicar, of course, was well aware any income from the soil had to be wrung from it somehow by this very odd collection of men who were the farmers of his parish. He also established a custom of giving every workman whom he had married in his church, a half-sovereign, after charging 6/8d for the registration fee. As the vicar said, they became better off for a very short time after marriage.

His Reverence knew all the best people and preached from the best book of sermons with perhaps more vigour than sincerity. His only sin apparently was to look down on the Squire when he should have looked up to him.

The vicar's contact with the Squire had had an unfortunate

'Damn Mrs Lee, where's the damned milk?'

beginning. Soon after his advent, he had arranged to give the pupils of the 'church school' a Christmas treat. Determined to put on a good show, he wanted it to be the Treat of all Treats. He procured a huge Christmas tree, loaded it with gifts, and provided a goodly supply of tasty sandwiches and sumptuous cakes. But he was a bad organiser. His intended programme was tea, presents off the tree, then games. Not only was Jimmy the warden unable to be there for tea, owing to having to milk his cows, but Miss Lamb, the chief Sunday school teacher could not come until six thirty as she was seeing after her sister, who had just given birth to a baby.

The vicar, unaccustomed to children, found himself with only junior female support when the crowd of children arrived in very good time. They began to play 'He' and to lark and scream, which agitated the red-headed divine to distraction. If only they could begin tea they would be quiet. But they could not begin tea because they were waiting for the Squire's wife to bring the milk from the Squire's pedigree Jersey herd. Fighting broke out and one of the table cloths was pulled off the table and the comestibles with which it was laden, were trampled underfoot.

Word was then given to the almost raving host that the Squire's carriage was approaching. Dancing with agitation, he met the Squire's imperious lady at the door.

"I am sorry to be late, vicar," she apologised, "but I called to see old Mrs. Lea who is at death's door."

"Damn Mrs. Lea, where is the damned milk?"

Now for an Edwardian vicar to address a Victorian Squire's lady in such terms was unforgivable. The Squire's family early decided the vicar 'would not do at all'. Nevertheless, 'everything comes to him who waits, if he only waits long enough'.

The vicar, being a bachelor, needed female help with the Mothers' Union and other parochial activities. Jimmy Oldfield's wife was too wily to accept a position where she would have to play second fiddle to her husband, and in any case, the new vicar showed a marked lack of enthusiasm for the Women's Temperance Association. The breach was admirably filled by the wife of an impecunious gentleman farmer. After marriage, this lady had rapidly produced a family of five and then enjoyed a period of infertility. She was a great success as the new vicar's right hand.

After a time, her long period of infertility terminated with the birth of another son. Though it was not yet apparent to the village, who knew what was going on, the new arrival had a head of red hair, and later developed a stammer. As the village said, 'to put the matter right', the eldest daughter of the impecunious gentleman farmer was married to the vicar. This presented an intriguing problem of relationship which was never properly agreed nor understood in the parish. The peculiar pattern of relationship, in addition to the disparity of age of the bridal pair, may have been the cause for a legal separation after the duration of about a year. The bride received a settlement of £400 per year, which was considered generous compensation for giving up the post of nursery governess which had commanded a salary of £25 per annum, in order to get married.

Needless to say, the marital difficulties worried the vicar excessively. He found himself unable to face his congregation in the church unless strongly fortified with 'Dutch Courage'. One Sunday morning, he was reading the prayers in fine form. "What an ass I am to be nervous," he thought, "I could go on like this all day." He made a sporting attempt. He began with the Litany prayers, continued with the Baptism of Infants, the Solemnization of Matrimony and Visitations of the Sick and when he reached the Burial of the Dead, he was led out of the church. He never returned and the Squire's wife was avenged.

***

Not surprisingly, these goings on shook the Established Church in Finchingfield and laid it open to competition. A powerful Evangelist appeared, to convert these undoubted sinners. Such was the power of his preaching and such was the repentance of his audience that the Evangelist proposed to hold a public baptism of two of his female converts. News of this reached the London daily via the same agency who reported the hailstorm which ruined the Gilby's crops, when their horses were struck by lightning at Foulslough Farm. The outcome of the report was a railway excursion from London to Braintree station, from whence the happy crowd were conveyed by wagonette to the scene of the baptism in Finchingfield.

It was a warm, summer afternoon, the crowd of visitors, locals and converts assembled in the natural amphitheatre of the village green which overlooked the river, specially damned for the occasion. At the appointed hour, the Evangelist appeared and waded to the centre of the stream. After an interval, his two converts followed, appropriately arrayed in full length black alpaca dresses with white cuffs, collars and caps. They proceeded towards the waiting Evangelist. As they went through the shallow water, it became apparent their black alpaca frocks floated on the surface revealing their white petticoats beneath. They hastily waded into deeper water and got into deeper trouble. Their voluminous skirts ballooned to the surface and they vainly tried to push them down to cover their shame.

At that time, for a young lady to show an ankle and a hem of a petticoat was to invite a titter from an indelicate male. The crowd were at first sympathetic with the ladies' dilemma, but the sight of the vain efforts to sink the ballooning alpaca was too much. Somebody laughed and that was the signal for a burst of uncontrollable mirth. The Baptism was perforce abandoned. It took place later in a remote flooded gravel pit for which those responsible paid a rent of one shilling so they should have the right to 'keep the public away'.

The Elders of the Chapel observed the invasion of the Evangelist with grave anxiety. After giving the matter due consideration, they staged a remarkable counter attack. They engaged an African preacher to preach at the Chapel one Sunday and advertised it well on the Finchingfield grapevine. Neither the young people of the village, nor their fathers, had ever seen an African man. When he finally mounted the pulpit, the queue to gain admittance to the Chapel reached down to the Fox Inn.

***

Before the vicar's matrimonial troubles, he had had cause to complain to Frank concerning his hospitality. That the liberal minded divine should have cause to protest occurred in peculiar circumstances. A neighbouring farmer was the son of a whisky distiller. In addition to liberally supporting his father's industry, he kept a thoroughbred stud. One night one of his mares was afflicted with colic. In the days before telephones, not having the necessary aperient, well charged with whisky, he rode hard on another horse to the vet's, six miles distant. He rode even harder on the way back and indeed, arrived in time to save the horse with colic. But the horse he had ridden dropped down dead after being dismounted in the yard.

This man always drove a very fast horse in a very light gig. One frosty morning the whisky drinker drove his freshly clipped horse to the village. He was quite unable to hold it or even turn it at a sharp corner. The horse crossed a green and plunged into a small pond covered with ice. Small though the pond was, with the confusion of harness, shafts and ice, the horse was drowned.

This horse-killer, being also a horse breeder, kept a thoroughbred stallion. In the spring this was led around the district to visit breeding mares. Old Sol, the stallion leader, like others of his calling, or even like his master, was fond of a glass or two. A new policeman appeared in the village and lost no time in informing all and sundry that he was going to be very much a 'new broom'. Patrolling the country roads, he came upon the thoroughbred stallion feeding on the greensward and Old Sol, grasping the lead, asleep beside it.

"Get up," demanded the law, without response. "You are drunk."

"Yes, I am."

"You are not fit to be in charge of this huge stallion."

"No, I am not. You take him."

"I shall lead the stallion home and report you."

The policeman set off. After a hundred yards, the thoroughbred stopped. A tug on the leader rein made the stallion rear up and knock off the policeman's helmet with a forehoof. It was fortunate indeed that the helmet was designed for protection. The next moment the stallion seized the victim's tunic with his teeth and tore half of it off. The law then called for the drunken groom to rescue him. This was soon accomplished and the groom led the stallion home, albeit somewhat deviously.

For some time after that 'hold my horse, sergeant' shouted round a corner near the patrolling policeman provided merriment for the village.

Now the horse-breeding whisky drinker, once visited Frank, who was so foolish as to offer him a drink. He had no sooner poured his friend a tot than Mrs. Green called to collect payment for her stone picking. Frank excused himself. Mrs. Green was very deaf but made up for lack of hearing by the use of her tongue. To settle with her took a long time and when Frank returned to his guest, the whisky bottle was empty. That being the case, the guest must perforce depart. Frank assisted him to mount his horse with difficulty and accompanied him down the drive, after which he seemed more or less all right. Farther along the road however, Frank's well oiled guest met the vicar whom he addressed thus:

> Mickey Mae Methuselah
> Married Noah's daughter
> And nearly stopped the flood
> By drinking up its water.
> And I would believe it
> Had the mixture only been
> But one half Glenlivet

couplets believed to be included in the unpublished works of the immortal poet.

The vicar, in spite of his liberal views, held Frank responsible for the state of his guest and administered a severe rebuke.

Not long after, Frank's guest became ill and a doctor was summoned. He made no bones about his diagnosis. "You have a stone liver (cirrhosis). You must give up alcohol and riding horseback or you are a dead man." The patient would do neither. A few weeks later, his wife woke up in the morning to discover her husband lying dead beside her.

IX

THE DEALERS

Around the turn of the century it was by dealing that the countryside lived. Money was scarce. At times farmers became desperate. Stories of crooked dealing abounded. Gussy Gatwood was a deacon of Finchingfield chapel. There was a time when prayer meetings were all the go and Gussy could pray with the best. Indeed, at one meeting, a lot of the supplicants had colds and Gussy's long exhortation was somewhat disturbed by coughing. He stopped in mid-prayer, rose from his knees and fixed the offender with a baleful eye. "How do you think I can pray properly if you keep making that infernal noise?" he demanded. He resumed, and managed to carry on 'til Amen time. But when it came to dealing he was 'a proper sharp one'. He seemed to have a nose for a 'softy'. Once he bought fifty whitefaced lambs of a breed that do not grow any bigger. Trade was bad and he could not sell them so he blacked their faces with black-lead stove polish and sold them off to Byford who thought they were half-bred Suffolks and would grow to twelve stone instead of six. The poor old man could not see very well and was too simple to notice the lamb's legs were white.

Gussy met his match, however, when he called on Old Nick Oaks. One day he drove into Coleman's Farm stable yard when Old Nick was there. "Good morning, Mr. Oaks," he called, "have you anything to sell?"

"Yes," said Nick, "I will sell you my hunter."

If Gussy had had a grain of sense he would have replied that he was not in want of a nag. Old Nick had never been keen to sell anything without very good reason. Instead, Gussy waited while Nick hollered to the groom to saddle the chestnut horse. Out he came with the nag, sixteen-two and with hard looking legs. His coat gleamed like silk in the sun. Gussy began to think of a dealer he knew in Leicestershire who could place such a horse around the £200 mark. Nick shut the iron gate leading out of the stable yard. "Git up, boy", he ordered the groom, "hold tight!" and gave the thoroughbred an almighty cut with his whip.

The horse plunged across the yard and cleared the five foot gate like a bird and disappeared down the road.

"My God," said Gussy, "that was a leap. What do you want to make of him?"

"Sixty guineas."

"I'll give you thirty and pay you now," countered Gussie, holding out his right hand for a handshake (In those days a handshake sealed a bargain).

"Done," roared Nick, giving the dealer's hand a blow like breaking the neck of a hare. He took Gussy indoors and gave him a brandy while he fumbled in a pocket deep ~ inside his waistcoat for the cash.

When they came out, the nag was back in the stable. It was broken-winded and could not gallop more than a couple of hundred yards before getting an attack of asthma. Nick had refused £3 for it from a knacker the week before. It was useless for any sort of work. Gussy had 'bitten his foot'.

Old Nick, however, found his match with Walter Hines, who also had a butcher's shop. Nick had twenty fat bullocks in a yard. Trade was bad and he would not sell them, so he kept them another year. His men kept littering the yard with straw till the dung got up to the top of the six-foot wall which surrounded the yard, and it got up higher than the mangers in which the bullocks were Nick had to do something, so he got Walter Hines to look at them. Walter looked at these oversized cattle, they frightened him. Old Nick had a cure for that and took him indoors where between them they about killed a bottle of brandy. Then Walter called for his horse and trap and climbed into his seat as best he could. Observing the dealer's condition, Old Nick thought the time had come to clinch an advantageous deal.

"Take another look at the bullocks, Mr. Nash," he said, "give your customers a treat and buy them."

Walter took another look. The bullocks were parading high up on their platform of dung. To Walter they appeared to be walking on air and looked as big as elephants, indeed in his present state he began to wonder if they were not in fact half-bred elephants.

"I'll take £18 a piece. They are cheap," urged Nick, noting

the condition of the butcher was as fully ripe as he had schemed.

Replied Walter, "Mr. Oakes, I am d-d drunk, I never buy nothing unless I am s-sober. Good day to you." He gave his horse a cut with his whip and shot out of the yard.

Walter once employed a young drover to drive sheep from Chelmsford to Braintree for a farmer, who gave him a shilling for the boy. Walter said he would give him 3d and keep the rest for himself, "he'll only use the money to get drunk," he said. Alas, he was right. With gin at 2d a tot and beer 2d a pint, the boy was seen later walking unsteadily round the market place.

This was the great age of the sheep and cattle dealer. Vast numbers of sheep were kept on East Anglian farms, and markets had to be found for their progeny. Walter was one of the largest operators. He began as a drover or employee of a dealer, and was sharp enough to get into the business without capital. Even in the eighteen eighties and nineties, store cattle were driven up on foot all the way from Wales to East Anglia, where they were reared and fattened. Hines's droving business from Wales was worth £250 a year to him. He gained his success by dealing with the best people and dealing with the best livestock. He must have been a good judge of both.

**

Of a different type was Jimmy Perry. Always smartly dressed and knowing everyone's business, he rode around the countryside and paid the expenses of his mount by letting out doubtful hunters to his aspiring clients. He was once late to market and furious at missing some undoubted bargains. His delay was occasioned thus. His farmhouse was equipped with the standard privy with three seats, one large for the Master, one medium for the Missus and a tiny one for the children, rather in the style of the Three Bears. On this particular morning, the Missus had respectfully waited for her lord to take precedence before making her necessary call to the outhouse. When she eventually did so, she spotted a golden sovereign on the floor which she returned to her lord. He immediately felt in the peculiar pockets of his extremely sporting breeches and found them empty when they should have held seven sovereigns. The privy was searched and another two discovered in the crack in the floorboards. Now this privy was kept spotless. The seats and floor were regularly scrubbed but the whole edifice was built over a noisome pit which had not been emptied for years. The cracks in the floorboards gave the searchers a clue, and Jimmy could not attend market till his gold had been re-mined by the emptying of the pit and the sifting of its contents.

He was a hard parent and would beat the daylights out of his high spirited sons. An old iron dealer once called at Jimmy's farm in his absence. A son made such a good deal in his father's old iron that he also sold the horserake, not missed till haytime. The consequences were cruel. The son afterwards became a very successful steel salesman and once said he would "buy an onion and put in his handkerchief for his father's funeral."

***

Harry Broyd was doing a large business with Frank at the time. In spite of the very material help they were to each other, they had some hard bargaining. A half-hour's argument would end thus: "I'll give you seventeen pounds ten for the heifers and 'stand in' if I can make more than ten shillings apiece profit."

"Let me send you two hundred lambs. They will be sold for nothing at Wilton as there ain't a spark of feed on the Downs. That second cut clover you have on Marsh field is growing too rank for seed. It will double pay you to fold it off with sheep... Andrew Goodchild has twenty young in-pig sows. I can buy them worth the money. He has not paid last year's rent yet. 'Muck or money'. pigs have been muck long enough and grub is bound to be cheap after harvest when all these beautiful fields of barley come to the mill."

On one occasion Harry bought 20 fat hogs from Frank. He picked them out of a lot of 40 and marked them by clipping their tails, for delivery at market the next week. Frank had a hunting fall the day after the deal and was confined to the house. On market day he deputed his 11-year-old Ben to be up at 6 a.m., to 'hold the light', a paraffin lantern, and supervise the loading of the swine. In the pitch dark of the early morning, the hogs were driven from the yard into an adjacent stable with the aid of the hurricane lanterns. A road waggon was covered with a pignet and backed up to the stable door. Two men grabbed hold of each ear of the selected hog and a third would grab its tail. The two men then linked hands under the pig's chest and 250 pounds of struggling and squealing pork was lifted into the high road-waggon. It became apparent one selected hog was afflicted with rheumatism and was unable to stand. The eleven-year-old supervisor, advised by his helpers, accordingly selected the next largest hog as a substitute and hurried the waggon off on its three-hour journey to market. The pigs met a bad trade and Harry came out with a furious tirade the next week, it was "the first time he had been done down over a marked pig from Frank Smith. It did not matter about a hog being a bit stiff. Rich's slaughterman could cure any disease any pig ever suffered from, but he could not make a little pig big. That little squirt spoilt the look of the whole bunch and spoilt the trade for them".

Such was the first black mark Ben acquired in the livestock trade.

But Harry was not always complaining. Far from it. He would say, "we must have a reckoning. I owe you a lot of money. Long settlements make short friends." His business record made his clients his friends.

***

'Monty' was another operator in this salubrious trade. He would buy anything if it were cheap enough. When he was old he recounted, "I once bought a diamond ring at Corky's sale when they sold him up. The diamond was as big as a hazel nut. I gave eighty pounds for it. I might have had a hundred for it, but my wife would not let me sell it!"

During the First world war, Monty bought an elephant. His wife let him sell that. He had it slaughtered and sold for dog's meat and cashed a nice profit.

When he became old, his bullocks broke out and strayed into Finchingfield's allotments. A man arrived in Monty's yard. He had a wooden leg and walked with a crutch.

"You b--y old s-d. You knew there was a gap in the fence afore you turned those cattle out into your meadow. They have messed everything up that was growing on my allotment. You old b--r".

"There is no need for you to swear. I am insured. If you can prove I have been negligent you can claim and they will pay."

"I don't want your d--d insurance. I don't want your d--d bullocks on my allotment you b--r' You s-d. You...."

"I suppose", replied Monty, "if I am all that, you would be what they call a gentleman."

***

Before the advent of the motor car the only means of transport, except by boat or rail, was by a horse-drawn vehicle, and the sole source of power on the land till the advent of the steam cable cultivators at the end of the 19th century, was also the horse. Knowledge of horses was vital for successful farming.

Horses were subject to numerous diseases which made them unfit for work and many vices which made them undesirable. The army had multitudes of horses and had periodic sales of 'cast' animals which they very sensibly branded or they would have found themselves buying back their rejects.

Jimmy Perry used to boast he once bought the two worst 'kickers' in the British Army. After roughing them off for the winter, with plenty of spring grass they became fat and their attractive grey coats shone like silk. The period without work seemed to have quietened them somewhat and Jimmy sold them 'as they stood' at a summer horse fair for sixty guineas apiece.

Horse dealers, dealing in the most unpredictable merchandise, often enjoyed a reputation for craftiness. They sometimes had to give a warranty with a sale, the horse would be sold as 'sound and quiet in all gears,' A horse with a chronic unsoundness could and sometimes would be relieved or temporarily cured of some ailment to enable it to be sold with a guarantee.

A certain Welsh cattle dealer also dabbled in horses. He once sold a 'dodgy' one with a warranty and got sued by his victim. He put his case in the hands of a sharpish lawyer whose name of Jones recommended him to the Celtic trader. Jones won the lawsuit, but his client was staggered by the amount of his bill. Not only would he have been better off to have lost the case, but the bill contained a substantial item for 'tobacco money', a professional term for 'purchased' evidence. The dealer paid up with a smile but, left the office pondering deeply.

The successful lawyer had hinted he might be interested in an exceptional trap horse should the dealer run across one. Back in Wales was an exceptional grey mare with a tender mouth and beautiful action. She was as quiet as a lamb for most of the year, but in spring, when her breeding organs became active, she could not bear trap harness to press on her rump. She had kicked two traps to pieces in two different spring times. Clearly she needed a change of venue. Accordingly, the dealer sent her to the lawyer on trial at a high price during the safe season. The mare behaved well during the period of trial, the deal was completed and the dealer paid. Early in the New Year the lawyer was driving a wealthy widow home in a governess cart after attending a quiet social function. The lawyer had handled her husband's estate, which was large enough for him to cherish designs of consoling the widow by becoming a successor to her departed spouse. Going downhill the trap hit a pothole and the resulting bounce produced the inevitable explosion from the mare. It was fortunate the governess cart had a rear exit or it might have fared ill with the driver and passenger. As it was, the trap was kicked to pieces and the romance wrecked. The mare was put down.

Next autumn the horse dealer was emerging from the 'Cups Hotel' when he came face to face with his legal victim who addressed him thus: "I have you in my eye, Mr. Evans."

"Indeed, Mr. Jones", replied the rogue, "and I have you in my pocket."

X

CAPTAIN AND CO.

In the 19th and early 20th centuries the sole source of power on the land, other than the rare steam tackle, was horsepower. Essex land was organised round two men and four horses per 100 acres of arable land. The shire breed of horse was almost universal. Except for its great size and strength, a more unsuitable animal for the Essex clay cannot be imagined. The shire had an enormous growth of long hair on his legs and, when the weather was wet, this hair picked up the clay and was most difficult to clean off, in spite of copious parading in the horse pond, present on every farm and generally the only supply of water for the horses to drink.

At Petches, Frank kept 9 working horses, including two or more young horses to be sold for town work when fully trained.

The first was Captain, too long in the tooth to be sold (horses ages were calculated by the state of their teeth), but active and willing for any work. Captain was careful to maintain his seniority over the other horses. Any of whom had the temerity to try to feed in his manger or come near his choice grazing in the pasture was shown Captain's teeth. Horses were more terrified of being bitten than being kicked. Captain was usually worked with the young horses to keep them steady and in line

Next was Gilbert, most reliable in the shafts of a waggon. When on a journey in a waggon he was wont to attempt to pull in the Inn yard at every Inn sign, hoping the waggoner would call for a drink and give his horses a rest. Depper came next, she would have probably been sold for town work had she not developed Monday Morning Leg. Highly fed horses in hard and regular work were adversely affected by the enforced rest on the Sabbath and sometimes came out with a huge dropsical swelling on one hind leg on a Monday. They did not go very lame and the swelling usually went down with exercise. If not reduced by exercise or work, the affliction always became chronic.

Next was Boxer, a showy horse with white socks and sometimes unreliable. Tinker, his mate, was the reverse and these two were paired up at plough so as to make them pull equally. Tinker had been docked very short. Most farm horses had their tails cut short. This barbarous habit may have saved long tails getting plastered with mud in wet weather, but in summer, when there were swarms of flies, the poor brutes were deprived of nature's protection. Tinker also had a very fine skin with a silky coat, and did the flies know it. One day when waiting in a dung tumbrel to allow a full load to proceed, Tinker jerked his head round in desperation to dislodge some flies on his flank and caught his bit on the shaft hook. Result: he backed the tumbrel and continued to back it across the road and down the steep bank into the pond, where he became suspended in the shafts. It became essential to free him as, if the tumbrel toppled sideways, he might drown. It was easy enough to free the drawing chains but the breeching chains were another matter as they were suspending ¾ of a ton of struggling horse flesh. Jack Faircloth, who had a hacksaw handy, sawed the breeching hook in two, the horse was freed unhurt and the tumbrel towed out undamaged. Jack then came out with some local philosophy, "I will go home, get my dinner and some dry clothes. If you never get into a muddle you never learn how to get out of it."

Punch and Judy were a younger pair and likely to be sold when horse trade improved.

Then came the freshly broken colts, just strong enough for a day's ploughing. The eight cart-horses had the capacity of four acres of ploughing per day and horse management was vital to keep pace with field cultivation.

Next came Nubia, Frank's renowned black hunter, by Old Sol's thoroughbred stallion from a draft mare. Frank had acquired him as a colt for little money on account of his colour. No gentleman would ride a black horse, it was deemed unworthy of anything except pulling a hearse. Frank recalled the proverb 'a good horse is never a bad colour'. Nubia was certainly a good horse. He was a heavyweight hunter with a beautiful action and had carried Frank on many a famous hunt. He loved jumping gates and once, when Frank was absent-mindedly approaching a gate and preparing to unlatch it with his crop, Nubia took a standing jump and cleared it, leaving Frank on the wrong side.

Nubia, worked by the half groom and half mechanic, would be called up to do a shift with the land horses, to work on the harrows and corn binder in busy times. It was Frank's practice to have two horses coupled to the pole of the binder. One of the two would be Captain with a young one or Nubia beside him. The men liked it when it was Nubia, he would walk faster than Captain and keep up a good pace which made the binder work more efficiently. The necessary third horse would be 'in trace' in front but had to be ridden by a boy. Ben, from a very early age, filled the job. The trace horse would keep the young horses straight, and Ben out of mischief. Frank's regard for Nubia was such that in the First World War a friend asked the loan of him for a day's hunting for his son, who was on leave from France. Frank refused with the excuse that the horse was lame. Frank, though he would do almost anything for a serving soldier, would no more lend Nubia than lend his wife. This was the cause of the only recorded untruth by his owner. Nubia was never put into shafts and Frank had a hackney to travel to the weekly market in his gig. The hackney was 'touched in the wind' or sometimes afflicted with equine asthma.

Next came Tommy, a Welsh pony for Fanny to drive in the 'tub' or governess cart and ridden by the children.

Last of all was the donkey. Harry Broyd once sent Frank 20 fine Irish steers, plus this donkey. It had always run with the steers in Ireland and the dealer had been forced to buy him to obtain the bunch and so the donkey passed on to Frank. An obliging uncle provided a small saddle and bridle and Frank's children proceeded to 'break him in' in the bullock yard, helped by the stockman. Alas, the donkey had a full share of his native perversity and always threw his rider. The dung in the bullock yard was too soft for this ejection to discourage the children, but bullock's excreta on their second-best clothes made the exercise unpopular with their mother. Frank hated this donkey, regarding it as an international badge of poverty. When the First World War broke out soon after, the farmers organised a gift sale in aid of the Red Cross and the donkey was the first lot; it made £5.

George Sorrel was in charge of the farm horses. Immensely strong and energetic, with iron nerves, he was possessed of endless patience with animals with whom he was always very quiet. Horses would do anything for him. The vicar once called on Frank when he was out and looked over the stable door as George was grooming his horses. After some conversation, George led Captain out into the yard. At the word 'Whoa', he stopped. George then walked round behind him and after Captain had stood still for five minutes, George said 'Gee up.' Captain then began to walk straight forward. At the word of 'Whoa-gee,' he veered to the right. At the word of 'Work-Mother' he veered to the left. At the word of 'Whoa', he stopped. Then George ordered, 'Whoa-back, Whoa-back,' and Captain walked backwards toward him until George said 'Whoa.' The vicar gave George a shilling with the remark, "if my flock were all so sensible and obedient they would all go to heaven."

George was a past master at breaking farm colts. They would be quartered at night in a yard adjacent to the older horses with whom they became well acquainted. They would then be haltered and fed in the stable beside them. By these patient degrees the colt would gradually adjust to work. Next stage was to fully harness the horse and make him stand for a time in the stable. He would then 'lunge' them, trotting them in harness in a large circle on a long leading rein. When this exercise was considered learnt, the horse would then be hooked on by trace chains to a heavy log, and coupled to an older horse. At the word 'Gee-up,' they would both go forward and at the word 'Whoa', they would both stop. The colt soon understood and was soon sufficiently initiated to do a half day's work on a plough beside his older mate. George's golden maxim was never to frighten a young horse or make him nervous of strange surroundings.

When George was young he was the keeper of an insane man with a suicidal tendency, who had been driving in a Governess cart when the horse bolted. He had fallen out of the back door and suffered brain damage. Said George, "He once tried to choke himself with cinders. I had to wedge a piece of wood between his teeth and pull the cinders out of the back of his mouth. Another time he tried to drown himself in the horse pond." He lost this job when his patient strangled himself with his braces one night. So George came to Frank, who had trained him.

Frank purchased a harvest elevator to take the sheaves of corn from the waggon up on to the stack. It was powered by 'horse'. The machine consisted of a large horizontal crown wheel which rotated on a small pinion wheel attached to a counter shaft, attached to the elevator. The crown wheel was rotated by a horse, suitably coupled, walking in a circle continuously. The first stack to be built with this machine was an oat stack, a few kernels of oats were constantly shed in the process, making a small heap under the elevator. The next morning, Captain was found to have a severe attack of 'gripes' (colic). Frank administered a very strong aperient and ordered George to lead Captain round the meadow and not allow him to roll until he had a motion and was relieved. Horses' stomachs were liable to get twisted when the horse rolled with the pain of gripes. A 'twisted gut' was always fatal in a horse. Captain was bad and already showing some signs of a 'twisted gut'. Not relishing the sight of a horse dying in agony, Frank went off to Jekyls. He returned at mid-day to receive the message that the horse had had a motion and was better. The stiff aperient had scoured the horse's insides and his excreta contained a quantity of undigested whole oats. Frank reflected, "I should have told George! I should have known he would do that." Frank's horses were always fed on crushed oats. George had scrapped up oats, shed from the freshly harvested crop, from under the new elevator and given Captain a feast, very nearly fatal. Frank never told George what he had discovered, but he let the second horseman know that new whole oats were dangerous if fed to horses.

Every year, a week or two before harvest, Petches received the Wethersfield harness maker and his son, for a few day's work repairing and overhauling the harness. Broken straps and buckles were mended, collars relined and the harness anointed with some evil smelling black fish oil. The harness maker was a fearsome man and a hectoring bully to his teenage son, who was a member of the newly formed Boy Scouts. The harness maker sold Frank a set of silver plated trap harness which had belonged to Marcus Pryke, before he gambled his farm away at an evening's roulette. The wheel and board on which Marcus laboured in vain to get rich are still preserved to this day.

XI

FARMING IN THE HORSE AGE

A good ploughman or drillman would not be more than four inches out of straight in ploughing or drilling a field four hundred yards long. Where the horse implements could not turn in the narrow angle, the best farmers would have the corners of their fields hand dug and hand sown.

Drills of young corn beside a road were carefully observed by the people of Finchingfield and the drillmen were justly proud of their work. Such a man was the young drillman of Harbinger Farm adjacent to the village. His fields of new emerged barley were a joy to behold. In the 'Swan' one evening he was talking to the eighty-year-old retired horseman of Shearcroft Hall, "and did you look at my fields of barley when you come down into the village, Granfer?"

"Aye, boy, I did look".

"And what did you think on 'em?"

"Well, boy, they most put me in mind of a little owd boy walking along a piddlin' in the snow!"

A day's stint of drilling was ten acres, which involved a walk of eleven miles over clods of earth. One day, Old Nick's horsemen asked for a half day off to attend a funeral. "You can go to the funeral after you have done a full journey with your drill", stipulated the martinet.

The men were up early to feed the horses and began drilling as soon as it was light enough to see where the drill was going. They finished their ten acres at one-thirty p.m., unharnessed and stabled their horses and were not late for the funeral.

***

Like most Essex farmers, Frank ploughed some of his fields on the two ridge stetch. The stetch would consist of four furrows ploughed one way and four furrows the reverse way. The two ridge stetch was an essential practise on 'wet' land, to assist drainage especially when early peas were grown for the London vegetable market. The necessary cultivations were carried out by implements adjusted to allow the horses pulling them to walk in furrows every seven and a half feet apart. The two ridge stetch work required exceptionally accurate ploughing, particularly in the marking out of the stetches by the ploughmen. Wilks, the pea grower, had on his farm a horseman renowned for his accuracy. With careful measurement he would set up a stick at each end of the field, drive his horses and steer his plough perfectly straight to it. He once suffered from a broken arm and his work had to be done by an understudy. In order to get his furrows perfectly straight he set five sticks in a row, when his senior had never had more than one. Sure enough the senior appeared to inspect the work. His arm was in a sling, but his tongue suffered no such handicap. "What? You planting a hedge?" he jeered, observing the row of five sticks.

**

A man would manage to 'get by' if he had a good wife and a good master. William Rixen was once heard to say that when he was a child his father would take bread and cheese in his dinner bag, his employer's farm being one and a half miles from his home. He had known his father bring home some of his cheese ration to toast for the children's supper. It may well be that William's mother saw to it her husband had a good big lump of cheese for his dinner, but such frugality, if necessary, could not have made a better supper for the children.

Nevertheless, being hard up did not diminish the sturdy independence of Frank's men. The same man was once sweeping the barn floor during a heavy rain. Frank was sheltering and conversing with his employees. Looking down he saw a silver sixpence on the barn floor. He picked it up and offered it to the sweeper, "Here, William, you had better take this. If you had swept a little further you would have found it, not me."

"Dall it, no, you keep it, master," came the instant reply, "the Devil always shits on the biggest heaps."

**

George had an exceptionally high standard of integrity. He once came home to Petches from a journey to Braintree after a day's work delivering a waggon load of barley to the malting. He had probably had little food since he set out at six a.m., and beer was stronger in those days. He had had some on an empty stomach.

When he reached the farm he so far forgot himself as to let Captain and Boxer drink in the horse pond still harnessed to the waggon. After they had drunk their fill, he found them unable to back the waggon out of the pond and had perforce to unhitch them. He fed and 'racked them up' with hay and returned to his cottage nearby. He had a very uneasy night and was up before daylight to pull his waggon out with horses harnessed with trace chains. He would not suffer the disgrace of his waggon being seen in the pond.

On another occasion, George discovered Gilbert had got into a deep ditch during the night. He was 'cast', lying more on his back than on his side and unable to get up or even to struggle any longer. Lying with his head upstream and in imminent danger of drowning, Gilbert's body was damming up the steady flow of water. George rushed back to the farmstead to gather as many men as possible to come and help. They first dug a sluice round the helpless quadruped, then quickly dug away the bank of the stream to form a not too steep ramp. Captain and Depper, in trace chains, were hooked to a rope round Gilbert's neck; it was impossible to get under his chest. A steady pull, and the great shire horse weighing nearly a ton, was soon lying helpless at the top of the bank. The diggers then all helped George to rub Gilbert hard with wisps of straw. After about ten minutes, to everyone's surprise, he got up on his feet, more or less unhurt. The sense of achievement and relief was expressed by the look on the faces of the men. It had to be seen to be understood.

Once Frank was addressed thus by his old horseman, "I suppose, Master, it won't be long before that horse dealer Emson comes along and buys these two young horses of mine. He will be a fool if he don't. They be the best pair I have ever broke, will do most anything I want, and in the way I want. What I'm a going to tell you is this. If you sell this pair and send me another couple of colts to break in, you must send a young man to do it. I be getting old and young horses be most too much for me now."

Frank knew his man and he knew his horses. Horse trade was bad. "All right George, if that is how you feel I will not sell this pair. You shall keep them here and work them as long as it suits you." Forty years of faithful service by the horseman to the family deserved nothing less.

After the old man knew his pair would not be sold, he groomed them till their coats shone like silk. He 'pinched' extra corn from the barn to feed them, perhaps too highly. After harvest and threshing, he set off to the station with a waggon load of five tons of corn. He had Captain and Depper in the shafts and the prized young pair 'in trace' in front. He was leading Captain and driving the trace horses with reins up the hill out of Finchingfield at a smart pace when they met Chapman's threshing tackle.

The traction engine was emitting clouds of smoke and steam and the iron wheels were making a fearful clatter on the road. This was too much for the highly-fed pair of young trace horses. They shied round, pulled the old horseman over, the waggon wheel went over him and he was killed.

***

For the first twenty years of the 20th century, practically all farms were ruled by the 'Four Course Shift'. This was a rigid four year rotation of crops which went as follows: a quarter of the arable land of the farm would be bare fallow or turnips and root crops, a quarter barley and oats, a quarter clover and beans or peas, and a quarter wheat. A large proportion of these crops were required for feeding animals. Oats were required for horse and cattle food, some barley and beans were required for feeding to all livestock. Clover was made into hay which was also fed to horses and livestock. As hay substitute, oat and barley straw would be cut into chaff and trodden into a bay of the barn, salt would be sprinkled as it was shot into the bay, spice sometimes added. The salt would cause a slight sweating and heating which would give the chaff an appetizing smell, if not taste.

For Frank's 30 bullocks, the best flavoured beef imaginable, the stockman would mix up cattle food daily in winter. He would fill four six-bushel bags of chaff. Being a good man, he would fill them by hand in as many minutes, then carry them from the chaff bay to the mixing house and shoot them into a heap. He would then clean a half a cart load of mangolds or swede turnips, grind them in a hand turnip cutter, and spread the shreds evenly on the heap of chaff. On top of this he would spread bean or barley meal and an equal amount of linseed or cottonseed cake, the residue from the oil pressing industry, sold in vast quantities in large slabs, which had to be kibbled in a hand machine on the farm. The heap of food was then thoroughly mixed with a shovel. The bullocks would be fed twice a day. Strong bullocks would be allowed a ration of 6 pounds of meal, 6 pounds of cake, and a bushel each of mangolds and chaff per day.

***

In those days every substantial farm in north Essex carried a flock of breeding sheep. Winterflood used to pay his rent with the sale of his lambs, and the sale of the wool would pay the shepherd's wages. Since he would never own a sheep trough to feed them concentrated food, he fed them entirely on crops they could graze and which he grew for that purpose.

Frank had a different approach. He wanted to keep the best fat lambs; maybe they were the most profitable. He therefore gave both his ewes plenty of purchased cake when they were nursing, and the lambs too, as soon as they could be taught to eat. The sheep would spend eight or nine months of the year in sheep folds on turnips, trefoil or white clover or red clover aftermath. The folds would be shifted twice daily. Frank used to feed a ton of cake per acre of folding. He thus got better and heavier lambs and improved the fertility of the soil. In the days before fertiliser, sheep were reckoned to have a 'golden hoof'. Heavy land was prone to be deficient in phosphate after centuries of cropping. Essential drainage was an expense which could not be met in hard times. Nearly all the lighter land had become acid after constant application of farmyard manure and from urine of folded sheep. The four course shift on poor land was a variation of the 'treadmill'. As Fanny's mother put it, "we grow the crops to feed the stock, to make the dung, to manure the land, to grow the crops to feed the stock..."

Nevertheless, in spite of the incredible effort needed, the very complexity of farming had additional rewards for those few who could cope adequately.

Winterflood, who never gave his sheep concentrates, may have achieved a profit. Frank, who was a heavy feeder, expected to get increased profits from his flock, also increased profits from the crops which followed. If better crops could be grown, the proportion fed to the same number of horses and stock to make dung, would be smaller and a greater proportion could be turned into much needed cash.

***

The farming year began at Michaelmas. Cultivation for the crop would commence with the ploughing in of beans and sowing the fallow with wheat. In September and October the clover seed crop would be harvested. Since clover only produced a successful crop of seed about every third year, Frank made a custom of buying Fanny a new frock when this occurred.

The threshing tackle would arrive and thresh two or three corn stacks to provide necessary cash. The threshing tackle consisted of a steam traction engine, a 'barn works' or threshing drum, an elevator to build the straw stack and a chaff cutter if required. It needed ten men to work a threshing tackle properly. Two, with pitch forks, would pitch the sheaves on to the top of the barn works. Here one man would pick up the sheaves and throw to the 'feeder', cutting the binding string as he did so. The feeder had to feed the broken sheaf evenly into the threshing drum. This complex machine knocked out the grains of corn and separated them from the chaff and straw by a system of sieves and a powerful fan. The threshed corn was delivered into sacks which the engine driver, if he were a good man, would change as they were filled. The chaff was blown through a separate spout into bags in a narrow alley between the barn works and the corn stack. The fan produced an appalling dust and the 'chaffey' was usually a boy or a very old man who would be unable to refuse this unpleasant but light task. The threshed straw would be delivered into the elevator, which took it to the straw stack built by two men. The two sheaf pitchers would require help as the corn stack 'got down', at the same time as the straw stackers required help as the straw stack 'got up', and required topping up. Another man would load and cart the corn to the barn, the chaff to the stable, fill and fetch loads of water from the pond, and keep the engine supplied with coal. He would need intermittent assistance or regular help if output were good.

Four bushels of wheat weighed 18 stone; barley 16; oats 12; and beans 19 stone. Sacks would be 'armed up' from the ground to cart or waggon. Two men would each grab a bottom corner of the sack hard with one hand, link their other hands, lift the sack and tilt it back on to their linked arms. Then they would place the bottom of the sack on the waggon and push the top up with their linked arms. Only two strongish men could do this and they would be grateful for a third man to push up behind.

The stackyard at Petches was notoriously wet and soft for the very heavy engine, barn works and elevator. Power was transmitted to all three by a heavy belt from the engine. It was quite an art to line the three up accurately, as indeed they had to be. Once a bad engine driver, unable to do this, made a mess of the difficult manœuvering of the elevator on the soft earth. He had to assemble the whole gang, who stood with their backs to the frame of the elevator and at the driver's order, "Now, all lift!", they shunted it in to place.

Stacks of corn were liable to heavy infestation by mice and rats if left over to the New Year. Mice ran all over the place, including up the trousers of a sheaf pitcher if he hadn't tied his trousers round his boots with enough string. Even so, this horrid happening frequently occurred, the pitcher's language is unprintable. Killing rats was a sport which relieved the monotony of the hardest work in the thickest dust. Farm workers on the stack were as keen as the farm terrier. Frank paid a small reward for rat's tails, mole's tails and sparrow heads.

The whole operation of threshing was hard work and, if the wind lay in the wrong quarter, desperately dusty. Frank's men used to 'take' the threshing piecework. They would 'take' any job if they could earn 'time and a half' and get plenty of beer. Presumably they got enough beer because once the vicar came up the road alongside which Frank was having some threshing done. The team accosted the vicar and insisted on his climbing on to the stack and joining them in a drink. Once, Jimmy Green was returning to the village after a tiring day and called in at the 'Lion', but in stepping down into the bar, which was only dimly lit by candles, he stumbled and fell full length. Mr. Tucker regarded Jimmy's prostrate form with consternation, thinking of the threshing beer and his respectable pub.

"I shall not serve you with beer tonight, Mr. Green. We shall be having some very good company this evening," expostulated Mr. Tucker, "if you care to call tomorrow, I will serve you a free pint. But not tonight!"

After the threshing machine had left to fulfil a contract with another farmer, there commenced 'the barnwork'. The threshed corn would be heaped in the barn. To clean it free of weeds it was put through a 'dressing machine', a combination of sieves and fan. 'Dressing' was a job for three men; one to turn the handle of the machine and provide the motive power; one to fill the hopper; and one to shovel the dressed corn into a bushel. The last man relied on help from the filler to hold the sack open to tip in his bushel of corn, to weigh, and tie the filled sack. This would then be moved by a sack barrow and the dressed corn would be 'topped', that is to say, parked in neat rows of sacks, one on top of another, which of course had to be 'armed up'. Dressing and weighing up corn would keep three men very busy at the expected rate of forty bushels per hour.

Tom Fitch was somewhat simple and, sad to say, sometimes taken advantage of by the junior high-spirited workers. "I always get the worst work," he used to complain. One day he was delighted to be instructed by the boss to turn the handle of the dressing machine, who even stayed long enough to see he turned it satisfactorily. When the boss's back was turned, Tom tried to take revenge on his mates.

"Now I'll make you b---rs work," he announced, and turned the handle with all his might. By so doing he thought he would increase the flow of grain. Poor Tom was not aware of the 'hopper regulator' which controlled the flow, his high-spirited mates adjusted this to give themselves an easy job, and let poor Tom work himself out in the vain pursuit of vengeance.

***

Ploughmen fed their horses soon after five a.m., took them out in harness at six, plough till nine; return to the stable, bait their team, have their own breakfast in one hour; plough till two o'clock, bring the horses in to bait and have their own dinner in an hour; groom the team, rack them up with hay, spread straw for their bedding and return home themselves at five.

Clover and bean stubbles were ploughed as soon as cleared, and sown with wheat. Mangolds were carted off in October or November. Three or four men each 'pull' a row. They threw the mangolds into a cart, slashing the leaves off as they threw. Three carts were pulled by the faithful horses who knew the routine almost without command. One filled, one emptied, and one would be travelling from field to clamp. When the field was cleared the clamp was thatched and 'earthed up', that is, covered with six inches of earth to protect the mangolds from frost.

Autumn sowing over, weather permitting, the ploughmen ploughed all winter, first for the roots and barley, and then the stubbles to be fallowed, the grassy weeds of which would have been grazed by the ewe flock, supplemented by turnips and hay.

Frank's ewes would begin to lamb in January. A sheepyard was constructed of thatched hurdles with small covered pens round the outside. The large Suffolk sheep favoured by Frank, produced a fair proportion of twins. Unless these were penned up with their mother for two or three days, the ewe was inclined to lose contact with them in a large flock. Any sheep losing a single lamb at birth would have a twin or triplet lamb adopted on to her. The dead lamb would be skinned and the skin tied on to the lamb to be adopted. The foster mother would recognise the smell of her own offspring. The ewe would be shut up, or if necessary, tied up in a pen from which she could not see outside. She usually took to the strange lamb in a couple of days. The shepherd's hut, which Captain pulled to whichever place on the farm it was necessary for the shepherd to be to watch the flock, was a standard piece of equipment with ewe flock. Joe Parsley said that when he was a lad, he became a shepherd's mate during lambing for two years. Then the shepherd broke his leg just before lambing time, so Joe had the flock on his own and lived in the hut. "I never had my boots off for a month," he declared.

***

In wintertime, daymen would be employed hedging, ditching and digging land drains. At the end of the day they would always take home a piece of firewood on their shoulders, called, 'kettle wage'. Frank never discouraged this practice, he said it was a

103

sign of a good workman to be thinking of his wife's comfort.

Dung carting took up a considerable portion of the farming programme. There would be the usual three horses and carts. Two men would fill the carts at cattle yard or clamp, another, usually a lad, would drive or lead the horses from clamp to field, and another man would empty the loads. In the field the load would be half tipped and cromed off into evenly spaced heaps, about 7 to a load. The dung was then spread and ploughed under. Two men reckoned to fill 40 loads in a day and then go home. Some farmers made a practice of having their muck clamps turned by hand. It was not unusual to bury a chain in the middle of the clamp. Those engaged in the laborious task of 'turning' had to produce the chain as proof of turning all the dung.

After the spring sowing of barley and oats, the mangold and potato land would be prepared. Double furrows would be opened up on the ridge and a heavy dressing of dung applied by spreading it along the furrows. In the case of potatoes, the 'sets' would be hand dropped on to the dung. The ridges would then be 'split back' and the dung buried. Frank would have a few rows of potatoes grown alongside his mangolds, allowing men with large families to grow a row of potatoes for themselves.

For mangolds, a light roller would be run over the ridges and the seed sown. Mangolds 'on the ridge' and turnips 'on the flat' were roughly side-hoed with a horse hoe, a job Captain was especially good at. The horse hoe was however, as crude as the hand hoeing was thorough. Hand hoeing was an incessant occupation in the late spring and early summer. Thistles and charlock in the winter wheat were attacked first. Docks were hand pulled or dug out with a 'dockspud', often by women, who also assisted in singling mangolds and turnips. Turnips were as often as not attacked, and frequently destroyed, by the 'fly' which consumed the seedlings as they emerged. Rolling with a light roller or dragging a sack soaked with paraffin along the rows were the only known controls.

Fertilisers were introduced at the end of the 19th century, *viz*, phosphate in the form of 'pure dissolved bones'. The poor old horse would spend his working life on the land. When he became too old to work, he was 'put down' and his bones were ground up for fertiliser. Another early aid to fertility was guano. In some dry regions, millions of sea birds had congregated for thousands of years. The vast deposit of their excreta was mined and shipped to this country to spread on the land. The first nitrogenous fertiliser in the form of Chilean nitrate was mined in South America. In the farming fraternity there was a strong prejudice against 'artificial manure'. Phosphate was said to encourage charlock, as indeed it did. Charlock, a cruciferous plant like the turnip, thrives on phosphate. Nitrate was said to 'draw the land and leave it poor'. Fertilisers were certainly unpopular with the farmworkers, who had to broadcast the dusty powder or astringent salt by hand. They often had to endure a dreadful dust whilst performing a very laborious task.

***

Year in, year out, the steady round of work plodded on from one job to the next, to the next, to the next. Hoeing and haymaking kept the farm staff occupied till harvest. After cutting the grass and curing it, the hay was raked and cocked in rows across the field. When sufficiently 'made', it would require a team of six or seven men to cart and stack it. The horses stood whilst two men pitched the hay on to a waggon where one man would load it. "Gee-up", they'd call, and the huge horse would haul the heavy waggon back to the farmstead. It was hard work, but not unpleasant as Frank provided plenty of beer for the men. A team were once carting hay when the man who was loading a fairly high load was suddenly seized with a violent fit. The two pitchers shinned up the rope cast over the load and held the victim down until he recovered. He always pitched after that. A high load was no place for a man subject to fits.

When not in use for haymaking or harvest, Frank saw to it that the waggons were carefully stored in the cart lodge. They must never be left out in the sun, the wind, or the wet. Apart from the necessity to protect the wood, the swelling of the wooden wheels in soaking rain, followed by shrinking in the sun, loosened the iron tyre. If the tyre came off, the waggon was useless. Should the tyre become loose during harvest, the waggon would be parked in a pond for the night to effect a temporary cure. Otherwise it was a job for the wheelwright.

He would take the iron tyre off the dry wheel, carefully measure the circumference with a measuring wheel, cut the tyre to the required size and weld the ends together. He would then heat the whole tyre as near red hot as he could and, with two helpers, carry it in tongs to the wheel, which would be laid out on a round iron platform. The hot tyre would then be levered on, and once in position would be 'squenched' with water, thus shrinking it tightly on to the wheel. It would be given additional fastening by being spiked on to the wheel with huge iron nails.

***

Harvest was always 'let' to the team at so much per acre. The bargain was to cut round the outside of the fields with a scythe and tie up the swathe; to trave the sheaves behind the binder, and to cart and stack the traves. When the stack was made, it would be thatched at so much per square (100 square feet). Men would stand out for a fair reward for this considerable job of work. Frank met the men and after they had come to an agreement, each man would receive a shilling 'letting money' to seal the bargain. The leader of the 'gang' was called 'Lord of the Harvest' and was pacemaker for the team.

As the fields were cleared, one trave in the centre was left if Frank wished to rake the field with a horse rake. This was a signal to the cottagers that the field must not be gleaned until the solitary trave had been removed with the rakings. The gleaners would come out from Finchingfield, mothers with whole families of small children. At the end of the day the heads of gleaned corn would be cut off and stored in sacks. When the threshing tackle came round, at the end of a day's threshing, the sacks of gleanings were put through the barn work. Samuel continued Old Thomas's custom of milling the gleaner's corn into flour, retaining the offal in payment. The gleaning family would aim at half a sack of flour, or even a full sack, which would make two hundred and twenty cottage loaves baked in the cottage oven. No mean achievement when money was so scarce.

Wheat fields were often not raked, as the binder made clean work of tying the corn up, that is, if it had not been beaten down by storms. Barley, being shorter and having an inverted ear when ripe, did not tie so well. The horse rake left the rakings in rows which were picked up at the end of harvest, often with a content of green weed. A boy would pull a heavy drag rake up behind the rows of rakings as they were cleared.

If corn was stacked before the green weeds had dried out, the stack would heat, and unless pulled down, cooled and rebuilt, could, and sometimes did, catch fire by spontaneous combustion. Frank's stacks were mostly round or boatshaped. The circle and curved ends reduced the distance which sheaves had to be pitched. Three men built a stack, one pitched the sheaves off the waggon as either Captain, Depper, Gilbert or Boxer patiently waited. The 'stacker' concentrated on building the outside walls of the stack. He layered the outside rows, bottoms outwards, and bound them in with rows of sheaves heads outwards. His mate would pitch the sheaves with a pitchfork to correct end forward ~ and pitched the sheaves for the middle of the stack so they were all in layers, with their heads outwards. When 'topping up' commenced, the mate retained a small stage, locally called a 'scaffold hole'. Here he received the sheaves from the unloader below, and pitched them up the roof. If a fourth man was not available, the stacking process was slowed down while the stack roof was built. The field team, who were under a handicap when the stack was low, now had the advantage.

Thatching straw was selected from the tallest and cleanest wheat from which the broken straw or 'carvings' would be separated at threshing time. The straw for thatch was 'shaken up' by tossing small forkfuls into a heap, and the heap continuously wetted with buckets of water. The straw was then 'drawn' by hand and 'yelmed' or combed. The 'yelms' were then tied into a convenient bundle and carried up a ladder to the thatcher.

Frank always had employment for boys at Petches. They could herd cattle, mind sheep, feed stock, clean mangolds, lead horses on horse hoes, and horses with waggon loads of hay or corn. Sometimes they drew straw for the thatcher. Frank once had a barn thatched by a professional thatcher. Straw was drawn and yelmed by the thatcher's two sons and a nephew. The latter was a tough diminutive child. Like some other undersized lads, he made up with aggression what he lacked in inches. This boy's father was a shoemaker who made boots for some of the people of Finchingfield. He was also an alcoholic and suffered from DTs. He enjoyed the distinction of having twice 'seen the Devil'.

The thatcher's son, however, taught young Ben how to prepare thatch, how to swear, and the rudiments of boxing.

The drenching of the policeman and the shepherd

XII

SALT OF THE EARTH

The most unpopular man at Petches and Jekyls was the shepherd. Maybe it was because of his unpredictable charges. Certainly he had an unpredictable temper. At times he had to have help, such as hauling his hurdles and food troughs to a fresh field of feed. This usually took place at an inconvenient time and the shepherd always put the hardest work on to his helpers if he could. "Old Shep spends most his time just watching his sheep feed in open fields, with a dog to do the running about for him," grumbled William, "you'd think he could haul a hurdle once in a while."

The flock was 'dipped' yearly, as required by law, a measure introduced to prevent the spread of 'scab', the scaling of the sheep's skin caused by a parasite. A wooden bath was hired, with a rack fitted with rollers. The policeman had to be present to check that each sheep was immersed for a full minute by his watch, in an arsenic solution of legal strength. The flock was penned and each sheep caught, turned on its back and immersed upside down in the bath, with a man holding each leg. Only the head was kept out of the poisonous dip. After the 'minute', the sheep would be lifted on to the rack and rubbed once back and forth along each side of its back respectively, the liquid being squeezed from its fleece and drained back into the wooden bath.

Suffolk ewes could weigh up to 250 lbs., and, if not held tight, would kick like pistons. The policeman rather welcomed the chance to show his authority on the farm. On one occasion a particularly strong, barren ewe, had been lifted into the bath. The law, in an unguarded moment, was looking at his watch and talking to the shepherd who was doing the catching with his crook. The two young men who were holding the ewe's back legs, let go simultaneously and jumped out of the way. The spasmodic kick by the ewe half emptied the bath in a shower which drenched both the law and the unpopular shepherd.

Maybe the real reason for the unpopularity of the shepherd was that he was a bad shepherd and everyone knew it. It was said in the 'Swan' that "if all shepherds was like he, there would not be much for butchers to do." Frank was most faithfully served in all other branches of the farmwork by skilful men, mostly trained by himself. He was constantly exasperated by this sole exception. He would never be told anything and always knew best. The time came when Old Shep's lameness got worse and he was off work. Sheep trade was good, Harry Broyd bid £1,000 for Frank's two hundred Suffolk ewes and they were sold. Frank put the cheque on deposit with the money left over from his fire insurance and began to think about buying a farm.

Farmworkers of that period were a tough, competent and pleasant crowd. There certainly always seemed to be plenty of them. The long hours of extremely laborious work could never have been accomplished without adequate nourishment, even if the food was plain, it was wholesome and sustaining. It is astonishing how far some men walked. Petches was three miles from Fred Lewsey's cottage. He would take his day's rations in his dinner bag and sometimes spend the whole day walking eleven miles on clods behind a team of horses before walking the three miles home again at night, a seventeen mile stint in all.

Men seldom left their masters or were ever sacked. Temporary employment was rare, though there was always a village 'workshy' who never wanted more than a 'sixpenny job'. Such a one was Abe Stockwell, only son of the widowed Finchingfield postmistress. She not only kept the post office, but also kept her son. Whilst he was a lad she had managed to get him a 'place' with most of the farmers around, but as he worked with more condescension than exertion, his employment was often terminated. For a period he had been sent to his uncle who was a vegetable porter in Spitalfields market. After going through all the boy's jobs at that salubrious spot, he had been returned to the post mistress. At thirty he was regarded as a 'slow coach' by the girls, and even more so by the young men. He seemed to be on a forgotten shelf as far as matrimony was concerned.

Frank, in a weak moment when he had an urgent gravel order to complete, yielded to the postmistress's request, and set Abe on to do odd jobs. One day a very suitable task appeared. Depper required shoeing. Depper must be ridden the mile journey to the blacksmith's forge and await her turn while shoeing was completed on earlier arrivals. After shoeing, the mare must be ridden home.

On this particular day, another young man was sent off to assist the stockman in carting straw to bed down the stock-yards and cart his mangolds. He was also given Frank's twelve bore gun to scare the rooks off Twelve Acre field. The gunner espied Abe returning at the end of the drive. Abe was sitting with both legs dangling on one side of the great shire horse's broad back, broad enough to make sitting astride uncomfortable even if more secure. From behind a thick, high hedge, the gun was fired into the air over Depper's head. She reared up straight on her hind legs in fright and deposited Abe on the drive.

Now Abe had brought home some undeniable London clothes and was currently 'looking over' the journeyman blacksmith's widow who had lost her husband with galloping consumption. The courtship was remarked on throughout Finchingfield and discussed in the 'Swan'. "He'll never git to marrying she, nor anyone else, he be too slow," or "she'll have more sense than have Abe, bad as she needs a man. He cain't keep she and her three children, 'taint so likely!"

Alas for the romance. At a concert in the Church Hall the current music hall hit was rendered. It immediately became a hit in the village:

> 'Abe, Abe, Abe my boy
> What are you waiting for now?
> You promised me
> You'd marry me
> Some day in June.
> It's never too late
> It's never too soon.
> All the family keep on asking me
> Which day? What day?
> I don't know what to say.
> Abe, Abe, Abe my love
> What are you waiting for now?

The village never stopped chanting this moving hymn, at least when Abe was visible. Mercifully for the widow, the Squire sold some oak trees and a burly timber feller arrived to fell them.

He lodged in Finchingfield. The widow fell for his brawn as quickly as did the Squire's oaks fall for his axe.

***

Jimmy Green was constantly causing amusement in the village where he was loved by all. A wiry, competent little man, he was always ready for a laugh, his only vice, if it was really a vice, was his fondness for a glass of beer. When the Petches gang received an issue of beer, Jimmy was deputed to pour out. He always managed to share the beer around and leave an extra horn for himself. When he was trimming a hedge, if he came across a young frog, and there were plenty in those days, he would swallow it whole. He called frogs 'the poor man's oyster'. It is believed he got more satisfaction from observing the disgusted expression on his revolted mates' faces than he did from this questionable delicacy.

Jimmy was married to a strong, capable woman, who was deaf. Having a family, though not a large one, did not fit well when the father had an unfailing thirst. His wife was, perforce, chancellor of the small family exchequer. They lived at 'Dinah', a thatched cottage about a third of a mile from Finchingfield. Every night, wet or fine, no matter how hard had been his day's work on the farm, Jimmy had to fetch two large buckets of water from the village pump. The cottage had no well, this was the sole ration of water for the family, including the weekly wash. To carry this water, Jimmy was equipped with a 'yoke' with a bucket hoop to hold the buckets steady. Sometimes after a hard day's work, Jimmy would combine the journey to the village pump with a visit to the village pub. Since anyone would buy Jimmy a pint if they had the money, and all knew his thrifty wife, he was usually able to assuage his thirst gratis. Indeed, if his friends were feeling flush, his legs were sometimes incapable of supporting the yoke with two large buckets of water back to his home. When the men in the village went to work at six a.m., and saw Jimmy's buckets, hoop and yoke hanging on the village pump, they knew Jimmy had made a night of it with his friends.

On one occasion, one of Frank's young horses had taken fright when being harnessed to a dung cart and Jimmy's hand had been jambed in the chains. He was off work and 'on the club'. Next Thursday the hounds met on the village green and Jimmy was in demand to hold the hunter's mounts with his uninjured hand, while they regaled themselves with Dutch Courage in the bar of the Fox Inn. When the huntsman blew the 'move off' on his horn, Jimmy's client remained in the bar sipping his drink. The horse nearly went mad with impatience as the hounds and field moved off, Jimmy with his one hand, held on. The owner then appeared and mounted his fractious horse as best he could. As Jimmy let go the rein, the horseman hastily thrust a sixpence into Jimmy's sound hand and made off on his bucking mount to catch up with the hunt.

Jimmy then adjourned to the bar. His friends had also been holding horses at the meet and as usual, treated their old friend with generosity. Jimmy in fact acquired a skinful without having to draw on his own tip. Making his way home on unsteady legs, he took the tip out of his pocket and looked at it. He could hardly believe his eyes. It was a golden half sovereign. In his haste and insecurity on his fractious horse, the hunter had made a mistake!

Now Jimmy was not so tight as not to know that his redoubtable chancellor of the exchequer would seize on this prize as soon as he reached home. How could he protect his good fortune from those masterful hands? Beer was tuppence pint. Half a sovereign represented more pints than he could count. Wait a minute though, did not rich people bank their money to keep it safe? Why should he not do the same? There was a bank on each side of the lane. Jimmy forthwith buried his gold in the roadside bank. It kept safe enough there, his chancellor never got her hands on it. Sad to say, the beer he consumed somewhat befuddled his outlook. He could never afterwards remember exactly where he had buried his half-sovereign and it probably remains there to this day.

***

Once, the seasonal round of work and gossip in Finchingfield received a jolt of excitement. There was a General election. The boys sang election songs and wore election badges.

The village shopkeeper was the leading Liberal. He was also an Elder of the Chapel and undertaker for the dissenting community. On undertaking occasions he wore a very long frock coat. Frank, a churchman, let it be known he would not mind being buried by this dissenting undertaker if he would but wear a black coat which reached to the ground. The shopkeeper was famous for 'pickling divine hams', which no doubt benefited from his undertaking experience. Indeed, a lady once requested him to 'embalm' a ham for her. He also possessed another important and indefinable quality. All the village entered his shop. He kept his customers and his trade without letting anyone get into his debt, no mean feat when most of his customers were on bare subsistence level. Everyone who entered his shop was his neighbour and friend.

The leading Conservative was, of course, Mr Tucker. His closest ally was Sam Turner, blacksmith and Captain of the Fire Brigade. Age and mechanical equipment had at last compelled Sam to give up this important status. During the election campaign, after a day's horse shoeing, he would change into his second best suit, adorned with a large blue rosette, and repair to the bar of the 'Lion'. Here he and Mr. Tucker would put the affairs of the country to rights, or earnestly declare what steps were necessary to this end.

Thus the leading Liberal dealt with the preparation for heaven, while his opposite numbers dealt with Fire and Brimstone. If the Lion's beer was not exactly fire and Brimstone, the Chapel Temperance Group thought it was.

Not only were there songs about tariff reform, adherents of each party sported artificial silk handkerchiefs embroidered with 'Vote for Tariff Reform', 'Down with Tariff Reform', 'Free Food for the Millions'. At this election the 'Free Food for the Million-ites' apparently had it, or as near as made no difference, for those of the countryside engaged in the production of food remained at near starvation level.

Jimmy banking his tip

XIII

THE MOTOR CAR

Round about 1907 the arrival of the motor car in the district was the subject of continual discussion on the Corn Exchange. Frank was wont to have his bullocks driven the ten miles on foot to market. To assist in this journey he used to send a capable and willing farm worker. One warm day, having safely penned his master's bullocks in the market, this young man visited a shop to purchase some much-needed ginger beer. He was served by the beautiful daughter of the shop-keeper, whose dark and flashing eyes 'basilisked' the attractive customer. He purchased a second-hand bicycle to repeat the visit, which was encouraged, and the courtship proceeded.

But one Sunday morning, the farm worker told a friend he was going to end this courtship. His girl was a shop-keeper's daughter. Their house was lit by gaslight, they even had a water tap over the kitchen sink. In Finchingfield there was no water which was not carried from the village pump, the cottages had candles and oil lamps for their sole illumination. It would not be fair on a girl to reduce her to these straits.

Mounting his bicycle, he began his journey to Braintree. As he proceeded, he was wondering how best to break the news to the dark-eyed belle and not looking where he was going. He descended Justices Hill and cut across the corner at the bottom on the wrong side of the road, he collided with one of the first motor cars seen in the district and was killed instantly.

Though the jury exonerated the driver of the car, at a time before insurance claims, a sum of money, (the village called it 'hush money') was paid to the dead man's relatives, as the car carried a foreign princess. The money was invested in a horse and wagonette, and a carrier service between Finchingfield and Braintree was inaugurated. Three generations of service to the public have turned the wagonette into a fleet of motor coaches.

Frank, after numerous journeys in his engineer friend's Darracq car, himself purchased in 1910, a car of that renowned make. Motor cars were temperamental starters in those days.

Frank was in the habit of backing his car into his garage, so the business end could be attended to in a good light when necessary, also it was then convenient for the much-needed and sovereign cure for the non-starters of that day - hooking a farm horse on the front and giving it a tow! The Darracq was equipped with some marvellous acetylene head-lamps which were fitted with large concave mirrors behind the burners. Now, Frank had a pet swan. It would take food from his hand and allow only him to stroke its neck; it used to talk to him in swan language. When the garage doors were left open, the swan was in the habit of waddling up to look at its reflection in the headlamp mirrors. This was condemned as female vanity by all except Frank who understood the lonely bird's craving for companionship.

On one occasion the car was driven into the garage, bonnet first, and sure enough, refused to start when next needed. After much cranking up, the engine obliged, and Frank hastily backed out. Alas the swan had seen the garage doors open and had come to have another look in the headlamp mirrors. Frank, impatient at his delay, hurriedly backed the car out over the swan, killing his pet, thereby taking a jaundiced view of motor cars ever after.

***

One of the Quaker flour millers not only had an early touring car, but he also invested in a Foden steam waggon to deliver flour far and wide. On a certain Saturday this steam waggon was making deliveries to Colchester which had a market on that day. Just as the miller drove into the town to attend the Corn Exchange, his car conked out. With the resource and economy of his sect, he sent a message round to the bakery for his steam waggon to come and give him a tow after delivering the flour. The corn market was not over until four o'clock and when the miller finally arrived back at his car, he found the steam waggon had been waiting an hour and a half and his two men anxious to get home. They towed the miller in his open tourer the 20 miles at top speed (15 to 20 miles per hour), constantly coaling up and blowing steam through the safety valve, thus subjecting their employer to a constant shower of damp smuts.

***

Mr Stratton, the coal merchant, invested in an early platform

117

lorry for delivery. He hit on the bright idea of also having char-à-banc fittings so he could hire the vehicle out for weekend excursions. Being an enthusiastic motorist and equipped with the most comprehensive motoring costume, he willingly undertook to drive for these excursions.

One of his first assignments was to take a party of ladies on a visit to Epping Forest. The afternoon was sunny and the picnic tea enjoyable. After the party had climbed aboard for the return journey, it was discovered that two of the ladies were missing. They had wandered off and got lost. The most careful search for them did not locate them for two hours. The return journey took much longer in the dark and Stratton arrived at his destination not far short of midnight to find a crowd of waiting husbands, who were almost ready to murder him.

The char-à-banc was not a success. Apart from the unlucky début, the open vehicle could only be used when the weather was fine. The roads of the day were mostly gravel and innocent of tarmac In consequence they were unbelievably dusty and, unless sheltered immediately behind the windscreen, motoring was only for the extremely hardy. Indeed, an early saloon, chauffeur driven, once crossed a hump-backed bridge at too high a speed. The wealthy owner, sitting in the back, was bounced up and hit the roof hard enough to break his neck.

Alfred Hutley purchased a second hand car, a semi-sports model, which had formerly belonged to a professional boxer. No farmer could then afford to buy new. He had it delivered into a large meadow where he could practice driving. When he had done this well enough to back it through the gate, he had enough confidence to drive it on the public highway.

XIV

1914. WORLD WAR ONE

Frank, Joseph Smith and General Sir Evelyn Wood were once hunting together in 1913. They were chatting at the corner of Lodge Wood while a terrier was trying to bolt a fox from an earth inside. Frank and the General were discussing the likelihood of war with Germany. Joe, the Quaker, bluntly remarked that he did not hold with all this talk of war. The Bible plainly directed that if a man smite you on one cheek you should turn and offer the other for a further blow. Sir Evelyn knew all about Joe's struggle to acquire his farms and replied, "Well, Joe, if I came along and took one of your farms away from you by force, would you then offer me another farm as a gift? That is what war amounts to." Replied the Quaker, "You may have the best of the argument, General, but no amount of argument ever made wrong right!"

The impact of the war on Frank's farming was significant. His team of young workers trained to 'have a go' at anything, almost all joined up in Kitchener's army. Frank's gravel side-line folded up. A buying commission arrived at Petches and commandeered a third of his horses. Off went Boxer, Tinker and the last pair of trace horses George had broken in before he was killed, leaving Frank with the aging Captain, Gilbert, Depper and a pair of young unbroken colts. Another buying commission arrived and commandeered some of his hay.

An odd thing about both the wars was that the Germans wished to traverse Belgium to invade France. In 1914 Belgium resisted and England declared war in support. The first effect on Finchingfield was the news of a large number of Belgian refugees who had fled to England. In a surge of patriotism and pity, the village set up a Refugee Committee. The whole place was canvassed for weekly subscriptions, an empty house procured and furnished with loaned furnishings. The larder was stocked none too soon, as two couples of refugees arrived from London.

The committee could and did house and feed them, but did not know what on earth to do with them. One couple were fortyish, exceedingly fat and spoke a little English. The other couple were twentyish, the woman fashionably dressed and attractive. French lessons were arranged for farmers' children with the fat pair. The charges for these were appropriated by the committee, which became a cause of friction.

Frank frowned on the whole project. Fanny hospitably asked the refugees to supper in pairs. Frank thought the fat pair would be better for a little less nourishment and rightly divined a loose screw with the young pair. For these, Fanny provided a menu which included home-made sausage rolls with very large sausages and very thin pastry. Frank noticed that the fashionably dressed female consumed three, but discarded the pastry. Though this may have been a sensible care for her attractive figure, in those frugal days it was considered wasteful extravagance.

The committee were soon in trouble. Two couples with little to do, could not agree in a small house. Moreover, it was rumoured the young couple were not married, at least not to each other. The effect of this news was catastrophic to the subscription list of the thrifty villagers and others pulled in by the indefatigable committee. For instance, a broken-down actor who was currently living with an Eurasian woman at the Pump House and having an affair with a married woman at the Tin House, was the first to refuse to pay his weekly sub, when news of the non-married couple got around.

It became clear to the committee that a more unsuitable cause for the thrifty villagers could scarcely be imagined. Presumably other homes and employment were found for the refugees, as they soon disappeared from the village scene.

Local patriotism was by no means extinguished by this awkward experience. A Red Cross committee was formed, lectures on nursing were given by local doctors, another and larger house was secured and organised as a hospital or convalescent home for wounded soldiers. The hospital was manned by a considerable rota of lady helpers and was, for a time, a great success. Later, battles produced such numbers of wounded that mass production methods of treatment had to be developed and the Finchingfield establishment was closed.

Frank became more involved with the War Agricultural

Committee, formed to encourage poorer farmers to produce more food and be the government's agent for any necessary food production regulations. He had the task of directing a 'Food Production Unit' of some of the early farm tractors appropriately named, 'Overtimes'. Horses, however well fed, groomed and managed, got tired after a day of hard pulling. A tractor never got tired, though, like a nervous cart horse, it often 'jibbed', that is to say, it would suddenly stop and nothing would make it go forward. The Unit had some of the early lighter Fordson tractors, driven by Land Army girls; the heavier 'Overtimes' were driven by ex-farmworkers seconded from the army.

The Unit was serviced by local engineers who had the busiest task. It was managed by local farmers and commanded by an extremely natty lieutenant, dressed in the poshest of breeches and uniform. He knew everything; that is to say, with one exception. After the war, he was engaged in the selling of shares in a non-existent company to produce cigarettes free from nicotine. He apparently did not know enough to keep out of gaol for fraud, of which he was convicted, receiving a two-year sentence.

The Food Production Unit was issued with a huge caterpillar tractor, one of a number especially made for the Russian government to pull Howitzers over the snow. When the Russians collapsed, these tractors were issued to Food Production Units instead. They were extremely powerful and had a tremendous potential, but had several drawbacks. The poorer farmers, whom the Food Production Units helped, were invariably small owners with fields unsuitable for large machines. Also, being produced for the Russian Government, the book of instructions was printed in that language, which no one in Finchingfield understood. Nor did anyone know how to obtain an English translation. But no instruction book could have corrected the open gearbox. The tracks picked up the soil by the hundredweight and deposited some of it in the gear box and slowly ground the gears out. They would probably have had a longer life with snow.

With the curtailment of Frank's gravel business, he began to look around for a larger farm. In 1915 it was reported on the Corn Exchange that the Stisted Estate was to be sold up. This belonged to Squire Stisted, who lived at the Hall in lavish style.

He kept 8 hunters, constructed a water supply for Stisted and built new cottages for the farm workers. He was something on the Stock Exchange and, of course, a member of the Essex Yeomanry. When the war came, he was caught in the resultant crash on the Stock Exchange and was called up for the Yeomanry. What was worse, the source of his real wealth was a large estate on the Continent in enemy territory, which was frozen. Stisted Estate, heavily mortgaged and unsupported from without, became a deadly millstone. It was quickly auctioned in over 100 lots and Frank bought the 360 acre 'Goodwins'. The tenant's agreement had two more years to run, so Frank had to wait before he could commence farming his new property.

The Squire was relieved of a burden, but bad luck dogged him without respite. After two bad bouts of trench fever, he was invalided out of the army. Came the time when a heavy instalment on his life insurance was due and the Squire could not meet it. He accordingly shot himself for the benefit of his family.

***

The war continued. One lot of troops after another would form up to join the special embarkation trains *en route* for France.

Guy Bedall, a ne'er-do-well farmer's son from Finchingfield had emigrated to Australia, joined the Australian army and taken part in the Dardanelles campaign. Coming home on leave, his account of his experiences in this fateful episode were certainly vivid: how the landing of troops was delayed by the gangplank being covered by an enemy machine gun: of his being blown up by a shell from the battleship *Queen Elizabeth*, "I was lifted high into the air and I could see my mates lying dead below," explained Guy at the bar of 'The Swan'. "The sixteen-inch shells of the battleship weighed a ton. After a time she 'split her decks' and was out of action."

Another less boastful returning soldier was Ernie Straker. A burly giant, he had joined Kitchener's army. He became a casualty in a gas attack and returned a coughing wreck. The village were all too familiar with T.B. and his condition was discussed in the Swan. The general opinion was that "Ernie ain't a mucher now. - He ain't going to do a lot of good. - He'll turn to a 'lunger' if he ain't one already." They were wrong. Mustard gas was apparently less lethal than the rod shaped bacillus, for after a very long convalescence Straker recovered completely.

One night after harvest, Finchingfield had a treat, being so fortunate as to witness a Zeppelin coming down in flames. As it proceeded on its stately and awe-inspiring way towards London, it passed over a primitive airfield. One of the English pilots 'pinched' a flying machine equipped with a machine gun which fired incendiary bullets. He cruised up to the hydrogen-filled monster, big as a church, and pulled the trigger. One incendiary bullet was enough. The hydrogen ignited and the Zeppelin exploded into a gigantic flaming torch. From the thousands who witnessed the conflagration and crash, no word of concern has ever been recorded for the crew who roasted alive in the gondolas attached beneath the airship. Rings were made from the ruin of the fuselage and were worn 'to bring good luck'!

In summer, 1917, whilst the children were at school, Frank and Fanny loaded their chattels on to wagons, and left Finchingfield. Captain, Depper and Gilbert hauled them up the hill past the Church to say farewell. The horses pulled them the 12 miles to Stisted, just 2 miles the other side of Braintree.

The eldest members of both Frank's and Fanny's families had inherited their family farms, Fanny had always felt Frank's elder brother dominated him. Now they would have a farm of their own. There would be no Squire to take their hard earned money in rent.

Their new property had an interesting farmhouse, built in the 16th century by a clothier, near Braintree, which had been an important centre of the woollen cloth trade at that time. The farmhouse was equipped with a brewhouse containing a rainwater pump from a rainwater well, a bread oven, an open fireplace and a washing copper - the brewing copper had been removed, but there was a goodly stock of crickets! In the scullery was a pump from the spring water well, with sink and primitive draining board. The kitchen had a huge cast iron range with an oven one side of the fire and a water tank on the other side, but hot water was not delivered further than the tap connected directly to it. In the garden was an extremely lordly privy, approached by a path delicately screened with copious shrubs.

Frank's first effort was to install some mod.cons., which he could enjoy knowing the expense was for his own benefit instead of his landlords', as at Petches. But the new farm was less productive than Frank had hoped. He had lost his well trained team of workers and everything needed was in short supply.

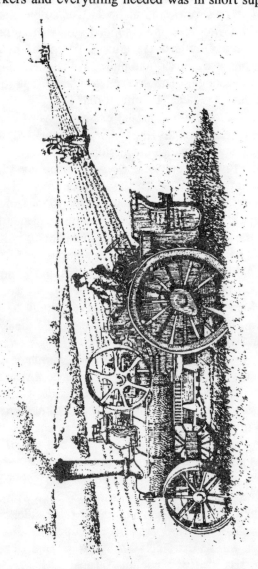

XIV

DR. HARRISON

Soon after the war, Fanny was taken ill with rheumatic fever and was attended by the renowned Braintree doctor, Harrison, who was universally acclaimed by his patients as the best doctor ever. It was said he was at times called in by other doctors to give a second opinion on a patient, and if he reckoned the patient would die, the patient always did die. His surgery was adorned with political cartoons and other moving decorations. For instance, the following notice was prominently displayed: 'D.O.R.A. All persons must order and pay for their own drinks. No treating is allowed'. During the Great War this notice had been ordered by law to be displayed in every public house in the realm.

He had a cartoon of a doctor examining with a stethoscope a very fat lady. The caption read, 'Say nine, nine, nine-pence for fourpence', to commemorate the birth of the National Health Insurance. His surgery door opened on to the pavement of Bank Street. Here he pulled innumerable teeth at a shilling per time. He also performed minor surgery with no anæsthetic, when "Hold tight, Mrs" would be the only preparation. When telephones were introduced, his number was Braintree 1.

Harrison was a bachelor and was assisted by a competent dispenser who seemed to enjoy observing other people's diseases and pains. He also had a competent secretary who kept his betting book, for the doctor was then the only bookmaker in Braintree. When Brigand won the Cambridgeshire, the doctor won enough money to buy a house, that still carries the name of 'Brigand Cottage', for his outside man, who always wore a brown bowler and a red waistcoat.

The doctor was a tremendous personality, which must have been the chief factor in his successful practice. He was also Coroner, an appointment by election, freeholders only being eligible to vote. First of all Harrison persuaded all his patients to purchase grave sites in order to qualify to vote for him. He was friendly with a famous neighbouring gunsmith who lived over the way, and who was a successful amateur Tory agent. They decided to issue an election address and had one printed. Some helpers were recruited to dispatch these on a certain Sunday. It was then discovered that only half the number needed had been printed. The gunsmith forthwith waited on the printer as he returned from Chapel. His indignant refusal to break the Sabbath and print some more addresses at once was met with equal insistence. The printer, though a Liberal, reflected. The doctor was very much 'The Doctor' and was also his doctor. Had not his friend Dodds nearly died of colic? Had not the doctor procured a surgeon from London who operated at once? Had not Dodds miraculously recovered? Anyone might get colic at any time! There was a prayer meeting at Chapel in the evening. If he went to that instead of the afternoon service, could not the printing be done at once?

He decided on this course of action, hoping to escape the worst of both worlds. Needless to say, the doctor's election was successful. He filled this post for 44 years, for which he was paid £272 per annum. During this time he held nearly three thousand inquests, including one on a whole gun team blown up in an artillery practice; another on the victims of an express train crash at Witham Station. During this enquiry the doctor stopped the proceedings in order that the Superintendent of the police could be awakened. In those days the weapon concerned in a suicide case was forfeit and became the perquisite of the Coroner. When Harrison died there were 32 pistols in his house, acquired in this grisly manner. It was recorded also that during the war, a man with a pair of 28 bore shotguns, shot himself with the first cartridge from a store of a thousand. Harrison was a keen shot and had his own preserve and keeper. He was so grateful to be able to appropriate the 999 cartridges, which were then unobtainable in gunshops, that he had the pair of guns sold for the benefit of the widow.

Harrison would not bother to charge a poor patient, but could be blunt enough with his more substantial clients if they did not pay. To one such, he recommended the purchase of a substantial property then for sale. "Why do you recommend me to buy that?" enquired the slow payer.

"It is right opposite the new cemetery. You could get a very cheap funeral from there - no need for the expense of horses and a hearse. A hand bier would suffice."

Knowing his man, he once said to Jimmy Perry thus, "It is gallstones making you feel so bad. I shall have to get a man from Harley Street to cut them out. It will cost sixty guineas and you must write the cheque before they give you the chloroform."

He liked to attend Mrs. Frank and regaled her with stories of his early connections with the house, where the owner used to pickle his hams in port wine, and once cooked one in champagne when it 'kind of sparkled in your mouth'.

Harrison made time for his exclusive practice in between shooting, racing and bookmaking. Once, he was called to attend a colleague afflicted with a septic throat. His tonsils were so swollen they were choking him. Harrison forthwith removed the tonsils, the patient taking a glass of brandy beforehand to steady him, and a hefty glass of sherry after the operation to revive him. There was no time, or apparently no need, for anæsthetics.

Though the doctor took days off, he never went away and only had two meals a day. He was a noted gourmand. He once invited the vet to dinner. The vet was of the same school of thought and manner. They began with plovers' eggs, obtained from the fields of one of the doctor's patients. "Have another of these eggs, John," invited the doctor to his guest, "it would cost you 3/6d at the Savoy."

"No thanks," replied the guest. "You eat it yourself and give me the 3/6d."

Harrison's fame gave him entry not only to the sick-rooms of the great, but also secured him choice invitations to their shoots. He was able to combine the results of the connections thus obtained, with the residue of his own shoot, and open a fish and game shop in Braintree, which was a great help to his sporting and gourmandising tastes.

His staff had a night off on Saturdays, when the doctor regularly took dinner at the White Hart. Understandably he was often late. The hotel changed hands, and the doctor received very much less than the usual attention which the previous proprietors had been careful to bestow on their distinguished client. After a cold, badly cooked and badly served meal, the gourmand's wrath was roused. The next Saturday he was later than ever. He had the dining room all to himself. During a long interval after the soup, the doctor pinned with drawing pins, on the underside of the table, a haddock obtained from his fish and game shop. After a few days the resultant stench rendered the dining room unusable. The stench was recognised as the kind given rise to by a dead rat beneath the floor. A carpenter was secured to remove a floor-board and trace the smell. The door being left open whilst he was working, a hungry dog was attracted by the stench. He entered the room and immediately gave the doctor's game away.

On the day of an important race at Ascot, the doctor wished to see an important betting acquaintance at the White Hart. As he approached the ancient hostelry, a very large new Rolls Royce pulled up outside. The driver disembarked. He was clad in a loud check cap with goggles and a very loud check suit to match.

The doctor's casual "Mornin'" was answered with a haughty stare as the important visitor proceeded toward the hotel dining room. The doctor paused to take a good look at the car. It was certainly an eyeful. A brand new open 'tourer'. Its highly polished paintwork reflected the doctor's face, the copious silver plating dazzled him. Moreover it was equipped with large electric headlights - the newest invention in the motoring world.

As the doctor finished his leisurely inspection, he became aware of an exceedingly dirty tramp approaching on the pavement, *en route* for the 'workhouse'. His tremendous beard and torn and dirty clothes proclaimed him to be one of the 'pea-picking fraternity', who had been sleeping rough under some hedge. The vacant look and starey eyes, to the doctor's experienced observance, betokened a methylated spirit drinker. "Hi, mate," he addressed the vagabond, "would you like to earn half a crown?" "Aye, master: What can I do for ye?" "Sit in my motor car and mind it while I have some lunch."

The doctor opened the door of the Rolls and installed the tramp in the back seat while he told him that he would have some change when he had paid for his lunch. He then went to the hotel bar, collected his betting commission and retreated by the back entrance at the bottom of the hotel yard, into a side street.

***

Though the doctor was fond of a practical joke, there was sometimes another side to the coin. The hounds used to meet at the doctor's favourite hotel. At one such meet there was a shot fox hanging up in the hotel yard to greet the hunt. It was attributed to the doctor. In the yard also there was a high game larder where a brace of pheasants were maturing for a special dinner the doctor was planning to give. At the end of the day, the hunt returned to the hotel before the hounds returned to the kennels. In the gathering dusk, the huntsman removed and pocketed the brace of pheasants from the larder, which he could just reach from the saddle. He then substituted the corpse of the fox and left his special compliments to the doctor with the ostler.

***

The doctor's game larder was the centre of another sporting incident. At one period the hotel was quite prepared to cook one of his hares to enable him to entertain guests there on the cheap. They had at that time no one on the staff able or willing to skin them. The doctor therefore ordered his keeper to skin and prepare a suitably matured hare on Saturday morning and place in the hotel game larder for the evening meal. This he did, but the carcase disappeared before it could be cooked.

The doctor gave his keeper some slightly different instructions. The next Saturday another carcase was hung in the larder and that also disappeared. When the theft was repeated on the third week, the doctor decided 'enough is enough'. He had a fair idea who the thief might be, and of course the theft was the subject of gossip in the hotel bar. On the third Saturday morning, the game keeper let it be known in the bar that the doctor had ordered him to shoot and skin a cat and place it in the game larder every Saturday morning. This he had been doing and the thief had therefore enjoyed a weekly dish of 'jugged cat'. From then on the doctor's game was left severely alone.

***

A local builder-undertaker drove his dog cart to Braintree to collect a coffin from a coffin maker, after which he stayed too long at the White Hart, where as usual Doctor Harrison was enjoying himself. The undertaker drank enough to pass out. "Lay him in the coffin in his dog-cart," instructed the doctor to a boy who agreed to drive the vehicle home. Added the doctor, "On arrival, ring the bell hard and disappear quickly."

***

The doctor was a frequent visitor to the Corn Exchange, where he could keep in touch with some of his patients and be properly briefed in the affairs of the countryside. On one visit, an acquaintance asked, "What's the prevailing state of disease?"

"Bad," replied Harrison. "I have three damned patients who are all going to die. One is Hutley of Dorewards who has a bad dose of typhoid. I order him to take nothing but beef tea. He takes beef tea all right, but with 50% Worcestershire sauce added. Another is Mrs. Frank Smith on the farm next door. She has a dose of rheumatic fever which would have killed most women before now."

Now Hutley was the kind of chap who even on his deathbed would have his ear to the ground and know all the news of the countryside. The doctor's report on the state of disease got back to him on the grapevine. In spite of the doctor's pessimism, he recovered, presumably thanks to the Worcestershire sauce. He paid a visit to Fanny, who was also slowly recovering. Alfred did not fail to impart the Corn Exchange gossip about the doctor's 'damned patients' to his fellow sufferer.

The next time Harrison visited Fanny, he was called to account. Said she, "Doctor, you reported you had three damned patients who were certain to die. One was Alfred Hutley and he is getting well. Another was myself and, in spite of you and the nurse, I am recovering. Who was the third damned patient?"

"Well, missis," replied the medico, "you say in spite of me and nurse you are better. Maybe you are right. I suppose I and the nurse did kill the third case."

"How so? Do tell me. I would like to know what I have escaped".

"Well, it was a bad bronchitis case. I took a bronchitis kettle along to make some steam and ease the patient's lungs. It was heated with a paraffin burner. The nurse set it going and went downstairs to cook some dinner. Whilst she was gone, the lamp got up and smoked. When she brought the meal up, the room was full of smoke and the patient suffocated."

130

***

Dr. Harrison's funeral was the biggest in Braintree. Among the wreaths was one from Aubrey Low; the attached card read, 'To Jack - till we meet again'. A sentimental widow did not know Aubrey was a notorious scoundrel and there was only one place in after life where they could possibly meet.

Taking care of the Rolls Royce

XVI

BEN'S BEGINNING

Farms were hit by a colossal slump after the First World War. The prices fixed for farming produce during the war were dropped, a flood of grain and meat arrived from abroad. Purchasing power of the industrial population was reduced by unemployment. In 1921 wheat fell from £20 per ton to £10 in one year, bringing down every other agricultural product with it.

A much respected local farmer who farmed 1,700 acres, reported his valuation of crops and stock was down by £12,000 in one year, and even then he had not allowed his accountants to show the whole fall. Young bullocks which had been bought to fatten for a year, realised less than their original purchase price.

Harry Broyd had a farming relative, and about that time Harry sent him 30 strong bullocks at £35 a piece. His relative had to face the same fall as everyone else, but did not pay Harry for the 30 hungry bovines. The same relative kept out of Harry's way for six years, after which the debt was 'statute barred'. He then called on Harry and had tea the following Sunday!

Behind the agricultural slump loomed a fall in all commodity prices. A family named Holt had removed to Yorkshire and there muscled into the wool combing industry. During the war they were in a fair way of business, their factory was supplied with wool by the Government who controlled all supplies. The time came when the wool control was to be stopped. The Government were going to release their entire vast stock of fleece wool. A syndicate was formed to purchase it at 2/10d per pound, rather lower than they had been paying. Holt was asked to join the syndicate and invited to the Savoy to discuss the terms of purchase. In spite of entertainment till the small hours, culminating in threats to run his factory out of wool, Holt would not play. He rejected the terms and refused to join the syndicate. The next day he booked a berth in a liner which was sailing to Australia two days later. He spent these two days arranging for very substantial credit in Lombard Street. He arrived in Melbourne just prior to the wool auctions. There he found the warehouses were full of unsold last years' wool clip, and the new clip was being sold by auction. No business had been done with England as the wool control was to be wound up. At the sale there were only two other substantial buyers, who arranged not to bid against each other. Holt claimed the record for the largest quantity of wool bought in the Melbourne sales. He bought it at 5d per pound and had only to ship it to England and undersell the syndicate, who were overloaded with stocks at 2/10d, to make a fortune. Bankruptcies followed and even a suicide.

Frank faced the slump with rigid economy and the assistance of his son, now aged 16. It was a bad period. Frank's horses and men were getting old. Farms must be mechanised with tractors and similar equipment. Neither Frank nor his men liked tractors which were very unreliable anyway. New equipment needed courage and new capital. Severe losses had to be coped with somehow. Moreover, his health became chronically bad.

Frank went to a sheep fair and bought 200 Suffolk ewe lambs. Asked the reason for his purchase, he replied it was to keep his son out of mischief. The sheep certainly did that, but gave the son a distaste for working hard for little or no reward.

After a bad year or two, Frank had to take careful stock of his financial position. On his new farm there was growing a large number of oak, ash, and elm trees, a status symbol of the 19th century landowner, but too many for efficient arable cultivation. The extensive woodland contained magnificent specimens of oak. As there was a fair demand for timber, Frank sold the lot to restore his finances. A team of timber fellers arrived and soon made the chips fly.

The huge trunks were hauled to a sawmill, partly by a small steam engine and by two teams of three horses. It was a pantomime to see the timber loaded by horses. The five ton trunk would be dragged to a position where the timber carriage could be drawn alongside. A stout prop was chained to the top of the front wheel and another to the rear wheel. These formed a ramp up which the trunk was rolled. This was accomplished by two long chains being fixed to the top of the props, threaded under the log and passed back over the timber carriage and joined. Three horses in trace harness would be hooked at length, onto the joined rolling chains. At the word 'Gee-up' they would all give a tremendous pull. The trunk would slowly roll up the props and on to the timber carriage. If the horses did not stop exactly on the shout of 'Whoa', the trunk would roll back down the props, or, alternatively, the team would pull the timber carriage over onto its side. There was always a tendency for the carriage to tip over anyway. A ground anchor held down by the horseman with a long lever, was often used. In this case, the horseman could not lead his horses, they would be directed by word of mouth only. The horses were of course, timber hauling every day, their understanding seemed uncanny.

Among the trees sold was a large, not particularly straight elm. It grew on top of a bank surrounding a 12 foot deep pond, with three feet of water in the bottom. The timber fellers were a skilful pair and reckoned to put any tree down where it was wanted. This time, a sudden gust of wind just as the tree toppled over, caused it to twist, it fell down the bank of the pond to the edge of the water. Some time later the horse team arrived to load the 5-ton trunk from the pond on to the timber carriage. The only way to get it up the bank was to roll it up. The team tried to roll one end up at a time and to attempt to keep it up with a hedgerow stump. Try as they would, it seemed the rolling motion always released the crooked trunk from the hedgerow stump and back into the pond it slipped. During these attempts the trunk was called everything big which begins with 'b', *viz*, "the boss should let the b - log be, till the b - pond filled with water and floated it to the top." Castration was a minor blessing they wished the deity, or his opposite number, to inflict on the timber fellers. Finally, just as it was getting dark, the horse team set off for the sawmill 5 miles away, with the trunk safely on the timber carriage, having, as Frank put it, "Run out of swear words."

The long tree trunks loaded on a timber carriage made a very large turning circle necessary, many of the farm gateposts became casualties. Frank did not fail to tell the timber merchant of this inevitable consequence, One afternoon one of the timber carriages arrived with a number of fresh sawn gateposts. "Your father has been finding fault with we," the horseman complained to Ben, "I have brought him a b - load of new gateposts. Tell him I shall be here tomorrow with a b - load of new post holes!"

200 tons of firewood from the tree-tops was the residue of this necessary financial operation; a 200 ton white elephant in fact. Fortunately for Frank, a prolonged coal strike then took place and the 200 tons was all sawn up and sold for firewood.

***

Times were so bad everyone thought they simply must improve; they certainly could not continue as they were. Older farmers gave up before they lost their all. Where the poorer farms were occupied by poorer farmers, bankruptcy became inevitable. Some farmers shot themselves when they could not meet their debts. The respected farmer with his 1,700 acres, a herd of cows, a flock of sheep and a steam cultivating tackle, went bankrupt for £50,000 in 1929. Poor arable farms became derelict, much of East Anglian arable land tumbled down to grass on which a small number of livestock subsisted.

At this juncture Frank's son, Ben, began to give trouble. "Something must be done about Ben," said Fanny.

"Do something? But what?" ruminated Frank, as he rode his old grey mare round the crops of Goodwins Farm. It was 1928, times were treacherous. How could Frank manage without Ben? Wonderful though Fanny's boiled mutton may be, and delicious was her copious fat home cured bacon, Frank's digestion was ruined. This, combined with chronic asthma was sapping his strength. Nothing the renowned Dr. Harrison could do could help. Ben was becoming restless, he had been helping his father for seven years and for what reward? What was more, he had fallen in love. He had joined the Braintree mixed hockey club. His hockey stick accidentally caught the ankle of the beautiful raven haired daughter of Mr. Stratton the coal merchant. For two years he had adored her. How could he even think of marriage? No home to offer her. No money.

"Do something about Ben? But what?" worried Frank, just as Old Thomas has worried about him.

Impatient with the old-established systems which could only have one end, Ben wished to have a farm for himself. It says something for Frank that with failing health and reduced capital, he was willing to give up his 'right hand' on his farm and finance him in an independent and doubtful venture. There was plenty of land on offer. Farms were cheap to buy, but no one seemed to have money to buy them.

On a nearby estate was a derelict farm of 400 acres, which was on offer rent free for two years, after which there could be a long lease at 5 shillings per acre. This was deemed too tough a proposition for young Ben to start on. It did find a tenant and his first crop was fifteen stacks of twitch hay. Though he was in the farm for ten years, he could never pay his bills without difficulty, was always behind with his trifling rent and could only pay the baker for his bread with 'poached' pheasants.

Another equally poor and mostly derelict farm was found nearby, 200 acres on which a rent of £100 was agreed. Ben began operations on 6th June, 1929, and contracted Johnson to cultivate 100 acres with his steam cultivating tackle.

The magnificent set of a pair of huge steam engines with cultivating and ploughing gear, plus a caravan, came at once. Their owner had ordered this set during the war, with the intention of accelerating field work on his own farm and paying for it by working around the district for others. The drawback was that delivery was delayed for years and the price much inflated. Johnson finally paid as much for them as the price of a good farm. One engine was christened *Peace*, the other *Victory*. They could and did do wonderful work in fine weather, manned by one driver for each engine, one man to steer the plough or cultivator, which the engines hauled from one end of the field to the other with a steel cable on a huge winding drum. They would also have a foreman who would relieve any of the three for meals in turn. Finally, there was a cook-boy to prepare food.

If work was plentiful and the weather fine, the engines worked throughout the hours of daylight during the summer. The men were paid a bonus on the season's work which would be around 1,500 acres. It was a busy job for a man and a pair of horses to cart the water and coal for the puffing giants.

Ben soon secured some horses, but not shires. He opted for the smaller chestnut Suffolk, not encumbered by long hair at the fetlocks, was easier to keep clean and more economic. Luckily there was an invaluable horseman who 'went with the farm'.

A more distant farmer had gone bankrupt and was being sold up at the time. Ben hired a one-ton platform truck and a driver from Mr. Stratton, and attended the sale. For the princely sum of £27/10/- he purchased a well-used Fordson tractor. With the aid of some disused gateposts, a shaky ramp was built up to the back of the truck. He then backed his purchase up on to the platform of the truck, relying on his brute strength to disengage the reverse gear and avoid demolishing the cab, as the tractor clutch was not working. The return journey was accomplished safely and he immediately set about following the steam tackle with additional cultivation.

The weather was hot and dry. Ben was glad to share a cup of tea at the steam tackle caravan. The older hand who steered the cultivator had been relieved by the cook-boy, he explained to Ben how they worked. "We get 1½d per acre bonus at the end of the season (November - December). That is what we reckon as our 'harvest'. I can then buy a new suit of clothes and some firewood for my sister who keeps house for me."

"Is that so?" the young farmer listened.

"You be careful what you say to our one-armed driver. He's quick tempered, especially if he had a lot of beer in him. Though he has only one arm, he'll fight anyone who puts him out. There is plenty what are afraid of him, but he can drive that old engine better than anyone, none the more for having only one arm. The boss has sacked him times for upsetting people. If he is sacked on Friday, he always turns up again on Monday. He won't go."

"Well, it takes all sorts," said Ben.

"You have one of these here bloaters for your tea. The boss always gits we a box of bloaters on market day and we put them up in the ventilator of the caravan. They keep nice and cool and keep sweet longer up there. Have you got any taters on your farm? We never reckon to buy any taters or milk either if we are working where they keep cows."

"How long have you worked on a steam cultivating set?"

"On and off since I were a boy and was cook. I worked for Brashy Brown for six years till he blew his old engine up."

"How did he do that?" asked Ben.

"We was a-moleing [mole draining], a wunnerful stiff bit o'

clay and Brown's old engine had not enough power to pull the drainer. Brashy screwed the safety valve down till the old ingin would pull it. Time the moler was a travelling up the field, everything was alright 'cos the engine was using the steam as fast as she was a making of it. When the drainer got to the top of the field, they had to stop and winch the drainer out by hand. The old engine didn't stop using her steam long, afore up she went. No one was killed but the flywheel was blew a quarter of a mile and the front wheels finished ten yards from the back wheels. After Brashy's ingin was busted he was busted too. He hadn't got no insurance nor nothing. I had to find another job and when Johnson got these engines new, I came along with he, and I been here ever since."

The steam tackle duly departed and Ben continued to stir up the resulting clods to finally kill the voluminous weed growth. The cheap tractor needed to be well understood. It started - ? - on petrol. After getting hot it was switched over to paraffin which was then very much cheaper. Ignition was provided by an arrangement of magnets affixed to the flywheel. The electric current so generated was then conveyed to some coils fitted with a make and break mechanism which in theory produced a spark in the sparking plug. The engine, if cranked up, would start only if everything was in perfect order and adjustment. It was also fitted with an air washer with the laudable idea of keeping dust and grit out of the carburettor and cylinders. If the water in the air washer fell below a certain level, the engine would stall, nor could it be re-started till the water level had been topped up.

One hot day, Ben was cultivating the clods on a field 400 yards long. It was nearly lunch time but he decided to go one more bout. Arrived at the far end of the field, a rather steep small slope down and up had to be negotiated. The tilt of the engine on the upward slope uncovered the inlet in the air washer and the engine stalled. The thought of trudging across 400 yards of clods and bringing water back to the stationary tractor, made the grey matter in Ben's head work. He wondered if he could? It was worth a try anyway! He stood up on the steering rod and spent a very useful penny into the air washer. The engine started 'first pull up', and he was not very late for lunch.

Another time Ben was working in a field near the street where dwelt a family of old iron merchants. They were gipsies who 'stayed put'. It was said their old grandmother was the boss of the outfit and she kept all the money. She condescended to bring Ben a can of tea and some plum cake. In between mouthfuls, he made cheerful conversation.

There was of course a small motive for this pleasant neighbourliness. The gipsies kept the usual kennel of lurchers and the fields which Ben was cultivating were their happy hunting ground for hares.

Later, one of the coils on the tractor packed up near the same spot. He observed some old coils on the gipsies' scrap heap and asked if he could try one to see if it would work. Certainly he could. It did work. Ben left his old coil on the heap in exchange.

A month later, he was repeating the cultivation of this field when one of the small gypsy boys came up to the tractor with a message that his Uncle wished to see him. Ben accordingly accompanied the child to the Uncle who was lying in bed in an open air hut. He was obviously dying from tuberculosis. "You had my coil for your tractor. You never paid for it," he accused.

Profoundly embarrassed, Ben admitted this was so and asked how much was the coil he had taken.

"Thirty-five shillings," demanded the invalid. Ben had not 35 pence on him and escaped with a promise to bring it after dinner.

***

Ben's first crop was good for those days, good enough to be too heavy for the 20-year-old corn binder given to him by Frank. Unfortunately the price of wheat fell from £10 per ton to £5 per ton. The higher price was less than the cost of most of the wheat then grown.

His speculation in sheep was more successful. Harry Broyd sent him 100 crone Suffolk ewes. Breeding flocks were culled of their aged ewes when their teeth dropped out. The ewes were then unable to bite sufficient turnips to support a lamb and were called 'crones'. These old ladies, after a lifetime spent in eating for the benefit of their offspring, ate for their own account to a purpose. They got fat on the stubble and left a profit of £100!

After this venture, a rival dealer offered him 100 in-lamb

shearlings, or 18-month-old ewes. "I can sell them worth the money if I can find a customer who can pay, but I must have cash," offered the old fox.

The sheep were well grown, young, and looked right to produce a good crop of lambs. Ben managed to knock two shillings per head off, for 'luck', and bought them.

It was not long before Harry called and took a look at his rival's goods. "They look wonderful cheap. I heard he had bought them from away, well worth the money. I don't know why he should sell anything cheap to you. They seem proper itchy. That one rubbing there puts me in mind of 'scab'. If you've bought scab you'll be in a muddle."

Scab was very contagious. It must be notified to the Ministry of Agriculture, who would put the farm into strict and prolonged quarantine. Careful observation seemed to confirm Harry's fears. Ben's next door neighbour had a concrete 'swim' dipping bath. After a word with him, Ben swam the sheep through the bath with double strength 'dip'. It was not the season for dipping and a Ministry vet travelling along the road adjacent to where the flock was grazing, became curious. He had the sheep penned and examined them carefully and took some tissue of the skin away for examination, which revealed possible dead scab parasites. In the meantime, the farm was placed in strict quarantine.

"We shall have another look in a couple of weeks," informed the Ministry vet. "When you dip you destroy the parasite but not its eggs. The farm must be kept in quarantine."

Ben took this all in and at once procured some more dip. He gave the flock a double strength dip at the right interval. The Ministry vet never found a live parasite. After this shaky start, the flock produced a useful crop of lambs.

It became clear that if wheat did not pay to grow, it would be profitable to buy to feed livestock. Ben was blessed with a very good neighbour who went in for poultry in a big way, who was kind enough to advise him how to keep poultry commercially.

At this juncture, Frank left the world of the living. He was laid to rest in the churchyard of Great Bardfield, not far from the mills of his childhood.

XVII

BRAVE NEW WORLD

So, within two years of Ben leaving Goodwins, his father was dead. And his fiancée, Winnie Stratton? Her father was described in one word by his customers, 'kind'.

"Too kind," said Ben, who in childhood had been told time and again of Old Thomas' experience with bakers who could not pay their bills. Alas for Winnie, many people could not pay for their coal, her father was declared bankrupt. Her mother became ill and was sent to hospital in London for an operation. Old Mr. Stratton visited her every day, a considerable journey from Braintree. He had a stroke and within three months was dead.

What hope was there for Ben and Winnie. Should they put their wedding off? Together they decided, no, the wedding would not be put off. They would marry and face the world.

Ben borrowed money to buy out his father's farm, moved from the 200 acres which he had hired and brought into cultivation, back to Goodwins. His economic philosophy on the venture was that, if an average farmer could balance his accounts, he would try to beat the average by 10%. This was to be achieved by 10% harder work and 10% better efficiency.

The bank manager told him he was marrying with a rope round his neck so he had to be careful it did not get too tight.

He developed a large laying flock of hens, a breeding herd of sows and a herd of cows. If the shortage of cash crippled farming accounts, then some way of obtaining cash had to be organised. Eggs gave the quickest turnover of capital, pork next, milk was a good third. Every evening Winnie washed the eggs for market. These, with the milk, produced a regular, if modest, flow of cash. Ben bought various foods and mixed them to scientific recipes. He paid as quickly as he could where discount was allowed and as slowly as he could where there was none. Concentrated food, being cheap, was fed liberally. The same policy was pursued with fertilizers for the farm crops. Most of the farmers who survived the slump had done so on fertile land and by spending no money. Ben sought to achieve a high output.

Fertilizers were then rather primitive. They were usually broadcast by hand since an efficient fertilizer drill was lacking. The young farmer soon discovered Goodwins would grow very good malting barley for which a good premium could be obtained. This crop must, however, be sown in the autumn instead of the spring. By so doing the barley gave a much higher yield of better malting quality. The only drawback was that the malting variety of barley would not survive a severe frost in winter. It was a risk which had to be taken.

The growing of wheat was avoided as much as possible.

Another discovery was that the farm would successfully grow early peas, to be picked green for the London markets a few days earlier than the average. By sowing with a wider space between the rows, the peas not only matured earlier, but they were easier to keep free from weeds with the aid of a sugar beet horse hoe. The Suffolk cart horses provided the pulling power.

There were a large number of tramps in the area at pea-picking time. As Goodwins was the first crop in the district, they flocked to the farm. This was equipped with a large thatched barn and cattle sheds way down the fields, a perfect place for tramps to camp. Ben used to thresh a field of corn and erect a straw stack near the barn. This served as bedding for the cattle in winter, and for the tramps in summer. A store of firewood was provided, to prevent the tramps breaking down the hedges for camp fires. Most of them had 'done time' and liked to get off the road, out of the way of the police. Ben once asked a gentle old man how he came to be 'on the road'. Came the reply, "I lost my wife. My son and his wife came to live with me. I became ill and didn't earn nothing. Time came when I couldn't stand that young woman's tongue so I took to the road".

The peapickers were paid a few shillings per bag for picking the peas, the money being paid in the field when the bags were tied up. One day some police arrived. They were looking for an old tramp with a red beard and a pram. Ben promised he would go and look in the field, but persuaded the 'coppers' to keep out of the way, as the sight of a blue uniform was liable to disperse the tramps like a flock of frightened rooks. He looked carefully and reported to the law that the man was not present. "What do you want him for?" he enquired.

"We want him for murder. He knocked one of his mates on the head with a kettle hook and killed him. He may have covered a good way since then, for we heard he was in this area."

"Well, don't tell my wife. I will let you know if I see him."

The poor old man was picked up in the next parish the next day. Apparently he had left his peapicking in a field for an interval to 'drum up', that is, to make a fire, and boil a tin of water and make tea to drink with his 'bread and margarine'. During his absence another tramp had purloined a bag of his untied peas and had drawn two shillings from the farm foreman for picking them. The injured man had enough of his earnings left to drown his sorrows that night in a nearby pub. On an empty stomach it needed very little alcohol to have a very large effect. Still raging over his grievance, he had returned to the lane where several of the tramps were camping. Under cover of darkness he had crept up behind the thief and hit him on the head with an iron hook he used to suspend his billycan over a camp fire. The loss of two shillings was a sufficient motive for murder.

On another occasion, a particularly nasty and aggressive family of gipsies wished to pick peas. Pea trade was bad. Ben was only picking a limited number recommended by the London salesman; just about enough to keep his regular pea picking crowd employed. These gipsies would not take 'no' for an answer and had twice been turned out of the pea field with difficulty. The following night Ben was awakened by a noise outside. "Confound those gipsies," he thought, "they think they can go to the pea field before it is light and when my man comes at five they will have established themselves. I will soon show them who is master here." He jumped out of bed, loaded a gun and without waiting to cover his pyjamas with more than a pair of gumboots, rushed out to repel the invaders. Instead of gipsies, he beheld the fire engine and fire brigade. His ire did not subside as quickly as the occasion warranted. The fire brigade were certainly not expecting to be met with a loaded gun. "Would you tell me what the devil you are doing here?" he demanded.

"We were told there was a fire."

"Well there is not. You should have rung my doorbell before you started to kick up such a row."

The fire brigade quickly took themselves off. Ben returned to his bedroom. Perhaps instinctively before getting into bed, he looked out of the window and observed a reflection over a screening plantation of trees, in the general direction of the barn in which the tramps camped. At the same time, some car lights approached down the drive.

The door-bell was rung hard and long. The police had arrived. "There is no fire here," Ben informed them, "but I think we had better investigate my pea picker camp."

They went down the fields. The thatched barn and cattle shed were burned flat, as was a large stack of wheat straw adjacent. Of the fifty tramps who had camped in the buildings, only three remained, one with a wooden leg who walked with a crutch, one who was badly burned and one who was attending him. The fire brigade was recalled and ambulance sent for. No further casualties were found. The injured man died the next day and it was only with the greatest difficulty that one tramp could be persuaded to give evidence at the inquest. The rest disappeared.

What had happened was subsequently reported by bush telegraph. The campers included a methylated spirit drinker. He had given himself a good dose before going to sleep in the heap of straw he used for bed covering. Waking up later, he groped to find his bottle of meths for another 'snifter'. As he had tipped it over before going to sleep, he could not find it. He then struck a match, in an instant the straw, anointed with meths, was blazing furiously. Everything was as dry as tinder and the thatched building and straw were consumed within minutes. The injured man had also had enough to drink to make him sleep too soundly to escape from the burning straw stack in which he had made himself a nest. He had been an engineer at the Morris Motor factory, and had fallen out with his wife and left her. She had been granted a maintenance order which he refused to pay. So he had 'taken to the road' and disappeared to avoid paying.

***

About 1932 the government introduced the famous 'Wheat Act', brought to Parliament by none other than the son of the Finchingfield Squire. The Act put a low minimum price on to this agricultural commodity. By the time it had become effective, Ben had learned to do without wheat. Nevertheless, it had a general beneficial influence on all farm prices. After ten years of disaster, agriculture could allow a very cautious optimism.

Ben bred up a fine team of Suffolk horses from his old mare Charlotte. Charlotte now had a foal, Kitty, a foal which grew into a mare he was never to forget. She worked hard patiently and faithfully all her life. As time went by, he had to learn to supplement horse power with tractor power. Fertilizers improved and the sugar beet crop was developed. After a hundred years of consuming imported sugar produced at first by slaves, and later by freed slaves paid on an equally low subsistence, English people now had some sugar produced on English soil in their tea. Ben grew his sugar beet like this: after careful preparation of the seed bed including a liberal dose of fertilizer, the beet seed was drilled. As soon as the rows of seedlings could be seen, inter-row cultivation was performed by a horse hoe. A boy would lead the horse and the horseman would steer the hoe. The rows of seedlings were then chopped out with a hoe and singled by hand, leaving plants ten inches apart. Men were paid piece-work. The price was one week's wages for one acre chopped out and singled. They could chop and single three acres in a week, though if the crop was not clean they would have to work hard for their money. After a few weeks, the crop would be second hoed and the space between the rows would be kept free from weeds by constant horse-hoeing. In October the beet lifting would commence with a horse drawn beet lifter.

The lifted beet were then hand pulled, the worst of the adhering clay soil vigorously knocked off and the beet laid in rows with a wide space between. Down this space proceeded a horse and cart, directed by word of mouth, while a man on each side of the cart chopped the tops off the beet and threw the root into the cart. The cartloads were driven off by the horseman to a convenient dump and tipped. The beet were then hand loaded into lorries and delivered to the factory. The beet crop required careful management, hard working and skilled farmworkers to be successful. Nevertheless, it provided a much needed cash crop in the arable rotation, responded to heavy dressings of fertilizer, but would not grow on acid land. It was the need of calcium or chalk for this crop which led to vast acreages of acid Essex land receiving the necessary chalk dressing to make it generally much more fertile.

About the same time, a straying dog from Braintree stampeded the sheep at Goodwins which were shut in a fold for the night. They escaped and were discovered peacefully grazing on a newly chopped-out field of sugar beet, which they had partially destroyed. Ben surveyed the damage with a jaundiced eye. "Golden hoof be blowed," he reflected, "what price their destructive mouths?"

Clearly it was time to get off the gold standard. He took the first opportunity to sell his flock. Sheep had lost their place in East Anglian agriculture and he was thankful to be without them.

XVIII

WORLD WAR TWO

'Air Raid Precautions' training was given long before war broke out. Ben and Winnie attended such classes and became acquainted with the probable unpleasant effects of phosgene gas, gas bombs, high explosive bombs, blast, and what have you, and learnt a basic first aid to deal with them.

On the Corn Exchange a young Quaker miller protested that all this training and talk of enemy action promoted hatred and mistrust and in fact provoked war. Replied Ben, "If you ever found yourself in a street hit by a bomb and people were lying wounded all over the place, your first and strongest instinct would be to help those who could not help themselves. People are quite useless if they don't know what to do. Trained, they can be a practical help." The young miller afterwards spent years in an ambulance unit in North Africa and Italy.

War was expected to begin with air bombardment of London and other cities, an attack with high explosive bombs mixed with gas and incendiaries. Stirrup pumps were issued to all farmers to deal with incendiaries and everyone was given a gas mask.

On the declaration of war, many women and children in London were evacuated to the country. The Goodwins' family was augmented by two small families in this way. Ben had a weekly squash racquets fixture with a friend in the Officers' Reserve. The week war was declared, what with the A.R.P. and other things, Ben forgot all about squash and played no more.

For a long time there was no bombing. For months there was a period of phoney war, confined to patrol activity on the Maginot and Siegfried lines, and submarine activity at sea. Most of the evacuees from the suburbs of London returned home.

Then the Germans attacked with their notorious *Blitzkrieg*, coming through Belgium exactly as in 1914. Invasion of England became imminent. Local invasion committees were set up and a very fine young army officer gave each parish in the Braintree district the 'form'. In Ben's parish the meeting took place in the church. "When the enemy came there was to be no civilian movement of any kind on the roads, whatever the conditions. Any civilian impeding military movements would be liquidated."

A store of 'Iron Rations' for the parish was established in Goodwins' cellar, where it remained throughout the war. ll signposts were removed. o car could be parked without removing the distributor rotor. ll service men were to carry loaded weapons. ll petrol pumps were registered for instant destruction. ransport was to be registered and note taken of any walls which could be pushed down and transported to fill up any bomb craters in roads. Any dead must be properly identified and decently buried. Apparently it was essential for morale for the belongings of the dead to be saved and given to the relatives. Indeed small bags were issued for this purpose.

The officer made all these grim precautions seem commonplace. His instructions would become law "when the balloon goes up". One old lady asked how one could be sure of seeing the balloon when it ascended!

After all these instructions to the civilian population on how the invasion was to be defeated, invasion did not come. The young army officer who gave invasion instruction then volunteered for service in an area where fighting was actually taking place, and got himself killed.

Although the invasion did not come, the Battle of Britain began in earnest, mostly above the clouds, out of sight, over the English Channel and Kent. The Navy had a effective rescue service right up to the French and Belgian coast, for any pilot baling out into 'the drink'. Whatever the proportion of losses of aircraft, the British thus established a very favourable advantage in pilots, who could not be replaced so easily as aircraft. As soon as the German airforce tumbled to this, they developed the habit of machine-gunning any pilot they saw floating in mid-air in a parachute. The British thought this was not at all cricket.

One morning Ben was on A.R.P. duty whilst an air battle was in progress above the clouds. Three parachutes appeared and were again screened by cloud. A military escort vehicle fitted with a machine gun over the cab, came tearing up the road. The soldiers enquired where the parachutists were as they intended to 'let them have it'. As they drove off Ben hoped the parachutists were not English.

It is now well known that air bombardment has to be very intensive indeed to be effective. It was reported there were a thousand bombing incidents in Essex before there was a direct hit on a house. It was of course, very different in London, which was repeatedly raided. The German aircraft came over Essex to reach the capital. Ben never once saw an enemy aircraft engaged by the British, but once saw a German Dornier, obviously hit, limping home unmolested. Later raids only took place in the 'blackout', that is, after dark.

One fine Saturday moonlight night, he was on A.R.P. duty when there were some tremendous explosions in the distance and one quite near, though out in the countryside. After the Braintree siren sounded the 'all clear', he returned home to find his house full of visitors, mostly employees and their families.

Apparently, some time after Ben had left his family at home to go on duty, there had been a knock on the door. Winnie answered the knock, but before opening the door enquired who was there.

"Please, it's us," came the reply.

Fortunately Winnie recognised the voice of Miss Cockerel, the poultry girl in charge of the numerous poultry flock. The door was opened to the news that there was an unexploded bomb near the workmen's homes. Miss Cockerel lodged with the tractor driver's family. Winnie became aware that 'us' totalled twenty people all requiring instant accommodation

Because of an unexploded bomb, the chief air raid warden of the area and the police had ordered about fifty people to evacuate and the road to be closed. Each family was given one room in the farmhouse; mattresses, blankets and rugs were shared round and presumably everyone got some sleep.

In the morning Ben questioned his men. One had dimly seen the bomb come down by parachute which was reported to have dropped just at the rear of 'Evegate', a neighbouring country house. It was a foggy morning. He advised the men to go across the fields to their homes and retrieve their Sunday joints and some more bedding and to open all the windows to minimise blast damage if and when the bomb exploded. This they did.

It became apparent that the neighbour in the country house had gone to some relatives, but had left his Jersey cow behind. It was essential to remove this cow from a bomb about to burst, and remove it so it could be milked. It would not come to a call, nor be tempted away from its home with a container of food. Ben accordingly walked across the field and drove it down to his farm. He observed a green parachute about twenty feet wide lying spread out just near the door of the Jersey's shed. It was a parachute mine. Whilst he was taking a good look at this, a delayed explosion took place in the distance and warned him to retreat. It was learned these parachute mines had been dropped all over Essex. Many were unexploded. The Bomb Disposal squads were dealing with them in strict order of priority; first those endangering factories, second those endangering vital communications and last, those threatening private houses. This bomb was the last on the list.

Apart from the organisation of twenty guests in the house, on the farm a crisis seemed likely to arise which would be paramount to war and home exigencies. Ben was digging potatoes for the London market. He was finishing one field and wished to begin another adjacent to the one where the bomb continued to repose. The female potato pickers manifestly would not work beside an unexploded bomb. But if Ben had to stop digging, he would lose his team of pickers who would go to assist another farmer, and he would lose his London customers.

On market day, in the Corn Exchange, a friend who farmed

nearer London; informed Ben that these parachute bombs were really magnetic mines. They had been made to lie in the sea lanes around the harbour approaches to Britain. A ship or two had been blown up, but the Navy had fished up a mine off Harwich and dissected it. It was fitted with a magnetic fuse which would detonate the mine as the ship passed over it. All ships were then in various ways demagnetised, and the mines were therefore useless in the sea. They were then diverted for raiding towns where they could cause tremendous blast damage in a built-up area. Each mine contained a ton of T.N.T. They were always loaded on aircraft in pairs, one suspended under each wing. The mines had a thin metal casing and the German pilots were understandably nervous of the 'flack' barrage around London whilst carrying this. They accordingly unloaded all over Essex before reaching the barrage. A naval officer had come to the friend's farm to defuse one of these unexploded mines. He had stripped to his shirt, taken everything metal from his pockets, and shod in gumboots, had unscrewed the fuse with a de-magnetised screwdriver.

"What size are the mines?" enquired Ben.

"They look exactly like a postal pillar box."

Ben returned to the farm and closely questioned his man who had witnessed the descent of the mine.

"No," he answered, "it had not hit the ground with any sort of a 'bonk'. When it hit the ground it made a kind of rattle."

Ben had seen the parachute and it had certainly been covering something, but nothing near as large as a pillar box. If the mine had partially buried itself in the ground it would surely have landed with enough force to make the impact heard?

Next morning there was another thick fog. The potato picking would finish by mid-day.

Ben took everything metal from his pockets, included his collar stud and tie pin, put on some gumboots and, unseen in the fog, walked across the fields up to the mine to investigate. There lay the parachute obviously covering something, but seemingly neither the size nor shape of a pillar box. He walked round it twice, and then, with the hair standing up on the back of his neck, took hold of the edge of the parachute and folded it back. It was covering a small water trough from which the Jersey cow was accustomed to drink! Of the mine, there was no sign.

He dragged the parachute across the meadow and put it on the back seat of his car. Driving to Braintree, he took the nearer 'closed' road and was stopped by the guard at the road block. Ben explained he had the 'mine' in the back of the car. The sentry, after a quick look, allowed him to proceed to the police station. His reception there was distinctly chilly after the announcement of the discovery of the 'mare's nest'.

The evacuees went joyfully home, to Winnie's intense relief, and the potato field was dug. The errant mine was subsequently located and exploded in some nearby woods.

All, apart from the war, was well.

***

A few weeks after this, although the air raid sirens had gone, Ben was lying in bed as it was not his night for duty. An aeroplane was circling around in a suggestive and menacing manner. "If that is a German I would not be surprised if he unloads about here before long," he said to Winnie.

Seconds later the house was shaken by a tremendous explosion. Ben was dressed and in his car within minutes and actually reached the scene of the incident before the duty wardens arrived on foot. A parachute mine had landed just down the steep bank of a pond a few yards from the rear of Peartree Farm, a 16th century farmhouse. The farmer had heard it and was opening the back door to investigate when it exploded. It blew his nightshirt off, but apart from being extremely dazed and shocked, he appeared uninjured. With his wife and two children he was sent to a neighbours to be cared for and put to bed. In the house was the old grandmother, eighty odd and bed-ridden. The blast had blown all the tiles off the roof and all the plaster off ceilings and walls, but had only shaken the old timber frame of

152

the house. The old lady lay in the middle of a king sized bed with the plaster of the ceiling all around her. She was in a bad way. In due course the ambulance and stretchers arrived with an important medical officer in an important uniform and helmet. "Lift her on to the stretcher," he ordered Ben. He took a look at the old lady, at the king sized bed, and at the medical officer in his important helmet.

"I think you had better move the old lady, Doctor. She is heavy and in a bad way. You know far more about this job than I." The sawbones perforce made the best job he could of the difficult task. The old lady was hauled on to the stretcher somehow and taken to hospital where she died two days later.

Ben got back to bed about three a.m. At seven the police telephoned with instructions to locate another mine which had not exploded, as they were always dropped in pairs.

After starting his farm men to work, he had another call, this time reporting the whereabouts of the mine. Ben went to investigate. The mine was standing up, in this case just like a pillar box, in a field, about two hundred yards from a road with a row of houses opposite. The police ordered the inevitable evacuation and reported to 'Bomb Disposal'. A naval officer and rating quickly arrived and investigated. The mine had come down with sufficient force to enter the ground about two feet. The naval officer explained that the fuse was below the ground.

"I want you to get a tractor, a very long wire rope, and hook a block up in that tree, lead the wire rope over it to give a lift, stand the tractor in the road, and haul. If the mine goes off we shall all be at a safe distance. If we can get it out of the ground, we can remove the fuse."

Alas, the Essex clay held the mine firmly. It would have been as easy to lift a gate-post out of the ground. A reduced gear was obtained to give a stronger lift, but then the wire rope broke. Ben offered to dig the mine out. His previous experience had given him a certain bravado.

"I am not too happy about using a spade, though I would

have thought your tractor pulling away would have triggered it off if it was going to explode," replied the officer, "I went to one last week which had dropped through a roof and come to rest in a cupboard. I was trying to get a sight of the fuse when I heard it start ticking. I ran for my life. Even so, when it exploded, the blast lifted me off my feet. I threw a spade against this one an hour ago, so it may not be very magnetic or it would have gone off. You go home and get your dinner. And keep out of the way for an hour."

Ben obeyed and returned with a camera. He was met by his old friend the police sergeant. "Let me take your camera, sir. It is an offence against the Defence Regulations to photograph any kind of weapon." The camera thus relinquished, Ben learned that the naval officer had removed the fuse. "You can dig it out now," said the officer, "I want it hauled to the road. I have a lorry on the way to take it to Woolwich for examination."

Ben did as he was ordered. When the container of a ton of TNT was excavated and free everywhere, he signalled for the tractor waiting on the road to come to him. This tractor was driven by a young man who came roaring across the field and pulled up short beside the mine. The carburettor emitted a hiss as the throttle was shut off. Ben thought it was the fuse of the mine which was hissing. He nearly jumped out of his skin!

**

When bombs dropped in a town they nearly always killed someone. In spite of this, people made as light of it as they could. A row of shops in Braintree had their windows blown out. They displayed notices, 'Open as Usual'. One had the message, 'More Open Than Usual'.

After one very noisy night in a country district, Ben asked a farmer on the Corn Exchange what had happened. "What indeed!" came the reply, "the R.A.F. put some dummy aerodrome landing lights on old Jim Chapman's farm and never even told him. About sixty bombs dropped. Jim spent most of the night in his cellar. He dare not light a cigarette for fear the

Ben thought the mine fuse had begun to hiss

Germans would see him."

"Was his farmstead hit?"

Not so likely. There are five hundred acres of Hungry Hall. The odds against the farm buildings being hit are five hundred to one. That ought to be a fair enough chance don't you think?"

On one occasion a canister of about thirty anti-personnel, or booby trap, bombs was unloaded in the countryside. Most were safely detonated by the bomb disposal squad. A farmer's son in that district was a bit simple. While ploughing a field, he spotted one of these little chaps, picked it up and put it in the tractor tool box. When he had finished his day's ploughing he took it to the policeman's house in the village. The 'copper' was out so he left it on the doorstep. The air raid warden saw it and sandbagged it to reduce the danger, it was eventually moved and detonated without harming anyone.

On another occasion, the very nervous wife of a farmer head warden was feeding her baby. The mother's help entered the room holding a small incendiary bomb. "Please, ma'm, the postman has brought this to the door. He wants to know if it has gone off or not!"

*****

One Sunday Ben was being shown round a friend's farm when a small aircraft came over, did a tight circle and crashed with a tremendous explosion. Ben was fairly experienced in pin-pointing this kind of how-do-you-do. He took a bearing and asked his host to return to his house to show him a map. They returned to the farmhouse and the bearing pointed in line with Goodwins.

Ben jumped into his car and rushed home. However the explosion was a mile beyond. It was the first flying bomb, otherwise known as 'doodlebug', to fall in the area. Later they came over often, only a few hundred feet up, with a tremendous roar. Goodwins was in their line of flight to London and in the area where the R.A.F. would bring them down if they could. It was quite exciting to see a Mosquito open up at them with cannon shells a few hundred feet up, but it made one hope that the doodlebug would land in a field. He had perforce to remember the five-hundred-to-one chance of Jim Chapman's farm, and keep his fingers crossed.

Once, a doodlebug was engaged just over Goodwlns at 5 a.m., when the cowmen were getting the cows in to milk. The cowmen crouched in a ditch as the Mosquito opened up. Later, Ben found some unexploded cannon shells embedded in the branches of a tree - certainly better than coming to rest in a cow!

British intelligence must have been pretty good, for a few days after the arrival of the first doodlebug, the Air Raid Wardens were given a lecture with a complete drawing, not only of the flying bomb, but also the V2s, or rockets. The latter made no sound until they exploded. Many dropped in the countryside short of their target, when there was usually a double explosion. The rockets travelled in the stratosphere. On re-entering, the atmospheric friction made the fuel tank red hot and the remains of the propellant then exploded. The warhead exploded on impact with the ground.

***

German intelligence was also pretty good. An aerodrome was built locally by the Americans in record time. For the foundations of the runways they used rubble from the London blitz. It was formally opened by an American Air Marshall one day, and raided by the Germans the next night. About twenty bombs were dropped, only doing slight damage. Most of the bombs dropped in a lake and killed the fish.

Land was requisitioned for airfields all over the place. Wethersfield, Gosfield, Saling and Rivenhall were examples of only some within ten miles of Braintree. Large numbers of Americans appeared in the district, the local population was asked to be 'friendly' towards them.

During the war, Ben farmed the old family place, Claypit Hall, for his uncle. This meant driving regularly from Stisted to Bardfield and Finchingfield. Ben's practical effort to be 'friendly' was mainly to make a rule of never passing a walking serviceman without offering him a lift. Also he offered to let American servicemen ride his horses, something which proved popular. On one occasion, some American officers, who had blown the stench of their Flying Fortress raids out of their nostrils with a good gallop round the farm, came to the door with a bunch of flowers and a large box full of chocolate, chewing gum, and thick gaudy comics for the children, by way of thanks. Ben answered the door and with an unusually quiet voice said, "Good morning."

"Ah gee, Mr. Smith, we've brought a few little candies and comics for your kids, and some flowers for your good wife," one of them drawled in a thick American accent.

"Thank you," said Ben, still unusually quiet, "my wife is with my daughter, I'll take the flowers to her."

The officers noticed his eyes were sunken and puffed, he looked 'real tired', they asked if anything was wrong.

"Well, as a matter of fact, my daughter is ill."

"Ah, gee! Nothing serious?"

"The doctor thinks it's meningitis".

"Ah, Mr. Smith, we're sure sorry to hear that, guess that's real painful."

"Yes," answered Ben quietly, "but sometimes she's unconscious."

The officers exchanged glances. They knew no drugs or medicines were available to the civilian population. They left in their jeep and, to Ben's surprise, were back an hour later. They knocked on the door and presented him with two little phials of M&B tablets, the new 'wonder drug'. These were administered to the sick girl who responded immediately and she recovered.

***

A very comprehensive War Agricultural Committee organisation was set up. There were District committees and a County committee. Their function was to increase the production of food to the maximum and to administer the livestock rationing scheme and other wartime regulations.

Ben was a member of a district committee. One of its first

tasks was to arrange the possible evacuation of coastal dairy herds in the event of a German invasion. The first thing the committee learnt was that all sorts of 'odd people' had become occupiers of farms during the 'bad times', many of them having only a vague knowledge of growing arable crops properly and, indeed, little wish to learn. Sad to say, some bought farms and called themselves farmers to evade conscription.

Much of the Essex land was unproductive grass which had to be ploughed up to grow wheat. To do this successfully required good equipment and skilful workmanship, often lacking. Farms were graded A, B, or C. 'A' farms were expected to grow what was required and to do it well, 'B' farms had to be carefully advised to bring them up to 'A' standard, and 'C' farms had to be supervised. If these did not improve, the land was taken away from the inefficient farmers. No one likes being labelled a failure and 'C' farmers were often very resentful of interference. Such a one was old R who existed on a farm almost derelict with neglect. The land was inherently good and something had to be done about him. He let it be known on the Corn Exchange that if any committee member came to his farm he would shoot him. The chairman of the local committee wrote to old R to the effect that he would call to discuss the state of his farm. The chairman took the precaution of taking Sergeant Cameron along. Arrived at the farm, sure enough the old man came out with the loaded gun. Cameron was a fine type of policeman. After a time, he persuaded the old man to give up the gun and listen to the chairman's explanation of their presence. The old man was eventually persuaded to hand over the farm to his son.

Ben had in his district a charming old man with a tiny farm which he cultivated with a pair of old horses. In consequence he was very hard up. He was a widower, further handicapped with a mad son, a tremendously strong young man who would never do a stroke of work to help. It was Ben's aim to persuade the old man to sell his old horses, buy a second-hand tractor and grow such crops as he was advised. Once when Ben was sitting in the farmhouse kitchen going over the proposed cropping with the old man, the son came in and threatened to shoot Ben, and looked as if he meant it. Ben was sitting in a heavy old-fashioned wooden chair. The gun was standing in a corner an equal distance from him and the madman. With the hair standing up on the back of his neck and gripping the arms of the chair tightly, he half rose and quietly but firmly told the old man to control his son. The old man shouted at the son, who after a time went out. Ben had been determined to push the wooden chair in between the madman and the gun, had the case been otherwise. He then gave a serious warning that on no account must such a thing happen again. The old man eventually had the son put into an asylum, and married a nice little widow. Presumably he lived happily ever after. If not, he made a sporting try, for he lived to be 95.

***

Ben once called, on agricultural committee business, at a small farm in a remote lane and could make no one hear when he rang the doorbell. So he went on to the next farm where there was a competent, pleasant farmer. After doing the business, he told the farmer he had been unable to get any response at the neighbour's door. "No, you won't either," was the reply, "there are two brothers there, both so nervously shy they'll not face a stranger. They have a peep-hole in the barn from which they can watch anyone they don't know. I'll come if you wish to see them."

"No, thank you. Their three fields look reasonably cared for. You let me know what they intend to grow and if they need any help. I am not looking for trouble."

One large farm was almost all grass and carried a milking herd and a flock of sheep. It was occupied by a pleasant but unsuccessful farmer who had a charming and competent wife. His was a 'B' farm and an acreage of grass was required to be ploughed and cropped. Ben had known him as a keen follower of the hounds and a successful point-to-point rider. He also knew that he had recently 'gone bust' on a farm in another district before moving to the local grass farm. Breaking up grass cost

160

money. It could be profitable only if cultivations were correct and thorough. Ben advised that one of the fields of grass to be ploughed should be sown with peas, and some others with corn. In order that the job should be done properly, he sent over his own men, disc harrow and drill. It was a productive season and a fine harvest. A splendid crop of peas was harvested in good order and realised a substantial price for pea soup, and the corn crops were also successful. The 'B' farmer thus had a hefty sum of money to take from his own crops for the first time in his life. He successfully applied to Ben to get him an allocation of new implements and never looked back.

What Ben did not discover until much later was that this farmer had been a member of the Advisory Committee in his old district, where he had gone bust. The chairman of that particular committee was the Hunt Secretary. He had insisted on having this man on his committee 'because he must have someone there who would vote to support him come hell or high water'!

***

Another wartime activity for which Ben's assistance was required was the organisation of 'War Weapons Week'. The purpose of this was to induce the massive purchase of war savings and defence bonds.

A parade was organised in Braintree, with a military band, a detachment of Australian soldiers, Home Guard, the A.R.P., the fire services, ambulance units, scouts, guides, 'Old Uncle Tom Cobley and All'. They were to be followed by trailers depicting various forms of war effort. It was a useful exercise in boosting morale, giving everyone a sense of having a stake in the united War Effort, prevented inflation, and provided finance to fight the war. Ben was asked to depict food production, and this was achieved by the building of a small thatched corn stack on one trailer and some sheaves of corn, milk churns and a live calf in a cage, on another. He was also asked to provide lunch for ten Australian soldiers, in those days of strict food rationing, a farmer's duty. They were an exceptionally fine lot of men, sadly afterwards mainly killed or taken prisoner in Greece.

The War Weapons Week was a great success in Braintree. The secretary of the effort was a civil servant of small size and even smaller capability or knowledge of the job. Nevertheless he was one of very many who during the war did strange jobs to the best of their ability. He was afterwards given the task of organising a Rural War Weapons Week and Ben helped with this too. In this case a number of village activities were to be organised and it was vital to enlist the active support of the farmers. Arthur Street, the agricultural author and broadcaster, was to address the farmers in the Corn Exchange. Ben was detailed to meet him off the train, show him round an East Anglian farm, give him lunch, bring him to the Corn Exchange and introduce him to the farmers at 3 p.m. After his speech, Street was to be taken to catch a distant main-line express.

On the appointed day, all began well. Ben found Street an interested and interesting guest, easy to entertain and appreciative of the organisation of an East Anglian farm. He was particularly struck by the sight of a hundred women picking peas for the London market. After lunch they went to the Corn Exchange which was crowded with farmers. Whilst Ben arranged to join together a couple of stands to form a platform, Street wandered off to chat with the farmers and merchants. The time for the speech approached; Street was lost in the crowd; there was only just about enough time to catch the distant main-line express after Street had said his piece. Ben was certainly in a fidget. A stranger in a clerical collar accosted him. "Are you Mr. Smith?"

"Yes, I am."

"I believe you are introducing Mr. Street here shortly. Would you please introduce me first? I am appealing for the Red Cross for Russia."

Ben regarded the cleric with disfavour. Several things went through his mind in a flash. He had heard that a local communist fifth column had started this fund since the Germans had invaded Russia. Could this upstart steal the hard-working little civil servant's party? Could he steal the great Arthur Street's platform? Could he bore the farmers with a sermon and make Street late for his train?

Not on your life! However, the sight of the clerical collar was enough to make Ben temporise. "I am introducing Mr. Street on the instructions of my committee. I will introduce you if my committee so instructs me," said he.

"Who is your chairman? Is he here?"

"Bill Oakum is chairman. He is somewhere in this crowd. If you can find him for me I shall be extremely obliged."

The cleric went off on a fruitless search. Street providentially appeared and climbed up with Ben on the improvised platform. Ben gave a hunting 'Holloa' to secure attention, and introduced the great man. He certainly had a way with him, the farmers listened sympathetically and with close attention to his speech.

The Rural War Weapons Week was subsequently an even greater success than the urban effort. The farmers more than came up to scratch. Ben hurried Street away and managed to catch the train.

In the evening, after loading the day's pick of peas of three hundred bags on to a lorry for the London market, a tired Ben was having his supper and listening to the account of yet another defeat on the war news, when the telephone rang.

He picked up the receiver. "This is the Reverend X. I found your attitude this afternoon very objectionable. Have you any explanation to offer?"

"No, I have not."

"Then I shall report you to my committee."

Replied Ben, "You may report me to the Devil himself," and slammed down the 'phone.

***

On another occasion Ben found himself chairman of a Farmer's Gift Sale for the Red Cross. The farmers of the district were canvassed for gifts, and all types of livestock and produce were offered for sale by auction. A few weeks before the sale, the enterprising secretary rang up and told him that he had requested a gift from Her Majesty the Queen, who had graciously sent the gift of a canteen of cutlery. The package in which it arrived contained a clear print of the Buckingham Palace postmark.

Ben received this news with a lack of enthusiasm. He well knew that the organisers' names would be mud if important gifts did not realise important prices at the sale. "Have it put down on the agenda for the next committee meeting," instructed Ben

When the committee met, he explained the position. After discussion, the richest man on the committee proposed that the minimum price in auction for the royal gift should be fifty guineas. This was carried.

On the day of the sale, the royal canteen was exhibited in a marquee and photographed by the press. Ben was too busy to have a look at it and had never seen more than the famous postmark. When it came up for auction the bidding was slow. Ben ran it up and it was knocked down to him for 45 guineas, the rich committee member having been notably and strangely silent. Ben's subsequent cheque included other purchases which he collected and took home before proceeding to a delayed inspection of the farm work. All being well, or as near well as a farm ever was, he returned home to supper.

Now, Winnie had an old aunt staying with her. This lady had recently retired from the post of companion to a well-known peeress. She continued in her retirement the close study of the Court Circular and other royal news, which had long been her chief interest. "Did you inspect the canteen before your purchase?" she enquired.

"No I am afraid I did not," he admitted, adding, "I've seen the Buckingham Palace postmark though."

"The canteen is of poor quality. I read in the newspaper that when Their Majesties visited the north they visited the factory bearing the name on the canteen. The paper also reported a gift of the firm's products to Her Majesty. It was most reprehensible of them to embarrass her by making a gift of such poor quality.

It was also most reprehensible of your secretary to trouble Her Majesty with the request for a gift. She must have innumerable demands. She may be acutely aware of both these *faux pas* and has taken a suitable means of getting rid of the canteen."

All this made the grey matter in Ben's head work. He rang up the secretary. "Put the royal canteen on the agenda for the final committee meeting of the Gift Sale," he instructed.

"I thought you bought that," replied the secretary.

"I bought it on behalf of the committee. You must remember the minute that it should make fifty guineas."

"I can't see how you can split up a canteen of cutlery," replied the secretary.

"No, but there are ten of us on the committee, we can raffle it at a fiver apiece."

The thought of being stung for a fiver must have made the secretary think. After a few days he again rang up. "Would you be willing to sell 'your' royal canteen?" he enquired.

"I don't suppose the committee would mind me disposing of 'their' property if it could be done profitably."

"If you would let me take it for him to look at, I know a certain party who might buy it."

"By all means. Call for it when you like."

The royal canteen with its original wrapper, on which the Buckingham Palace postmark was still intact, was taken to the certain party, who had seen the photograph in the press. One glance at the famous postmark was enough to make him pull £50 of black market money from his pocket, add the cash to make it guineas and buy it on the spot. Ben's bacon was saved!

***

On the farms, employment had to be found for the Women's Land Army, many of whom had been caught up in the universal conscription. There was always plenty to do on Ben's farms and he only stipulated that any girls sent to him must be either useful or ornamental, he did not mind which. He was extremely fortunate to obtain the services of a couple of girls who enjoyed both qualifications. They were not only a couple of smashers to look at, but would tackle any job of work. It may well be they were encouraged by the handsome young foreman who directed and instructed them. The old foreman on another farm tried to promote a match for his colleague. When he put the young man on a corn binder drawn by a tractor driven by a blonde in breeches and bikini he thought he had done the trick. He was mistaken. The young foreman was snatched up by a war widow and a little later he took a half day off and married her.

The attraction of working on Ben's farms thus ceased for the buxom and beautiful pair. One went to a doctor, complained of rheumatism and got a certificate of being unfit for land work in the Women's Land Army. The other went to another doctor and complained of every pain except housemaid's knee. She got a certificate of incapacity for farm work.

The girls then exchanged doctors, and each got a certificate of perfect fitness to enable them to join the overseas N.A.A.F.I.

***

Ben's miscellaneous wartime activities brought him into occasional contact with the Home Guard. There were always jokes about the Home Guard, as indeed about any other service. Of those who have laughed at *Dad's Army,* only a few are capable of understanding, much less feeling, the devotion to duty and unselfish patriotism traditional with the Home Guard. It contained some very tough and competent men and, had invasion taken place, the members of that force would have acquitted themselves honourably and effectively.

It was not all fun and games. Before the war, Ben's squash playing friend was a retired P.T. instructor from the regular army who was the nearest thing to a perfect sportsman and a perfect gentleman Ben ever ran across. He became a Home Guard instructor. At first they were all volunteers, but later, some odds and sods were raked in by universal conscription. The instructor had to teach the use of live hand grenades. One day he was in a trench with a B-F-, who had to pull out the firing pin of

'He mostly be down the field with that new concubine of his'

a grenade and throw it at a mark some distance away. He pulled out the pin and dropped the grenade. The instructor brushed past him in the trench, and picked up the grenade to throw it away. Too late: it exploded and killed him. The B-F - completely protected by the body of the instructor was - er, shocked.

On the land, great strides were made. The development of the combined fertilizer-and-seed drill, with the use of granular fertilizer, almost made bad land good. The sense of urgency and of being needed was a great stimulant to farmers. Production of corn so increased that the threshing tackle capacity was exceeded by the crops. Ben had previously relied on a contractor. After an attempt to purchase his own threshing machine, he was discouraged by the sky-high prices and he therefore bought a combine harvester. Like most new inventions, though it solved some problems, it created others and seemed to need constant attention. One harvest a stranger called at the farm and asked an old horseman, "Where is the Boss?"

"I don't know," came the reply, "he mostly be in the field with that new 'concubine' of his!"

The early combine was slow and only dealt with a part of the crop. Wheat, which could be harvested damp by traditional methods, was still cut with a binder, traved and stacked.

In spite of the advance of mechanisation, there were still, and perhaps are still, jobs which could be worked more economically with good horses. The trouble was that horses were only good if they had regular and constant work. With increased mechanisation, horses were subject to periods of idleness which were bad for their digestions and bad for their manners. One day after the war, Ben returned from market and proceeded to a harvest field where a team of young men were loading wheat sheaves on to waggons. Instead of a horse pulling the wagon it was being hauled by a tractor. Instead of going forward by word of mouth, one of the pitchers had to mount the tractor and drive it forward; a comparatively slow process performed by one man and watched by two. Ben asked the reason for the change.

"We have had one horse bolt with a waggon and another is not to be trusted. We are nervous of being on a waggon with a horse in the shafts."

"Young men afraid of old horses," thought Ben, "nice state of affairs."

To breed farm horses was a five or six year's operation. Eleven months from mating to foaling, three years to breaking in, two years to be fully trained, when the horse would command a price of £50. In those days the words 'Economics' and 'Viable' were unknown in the rural vocabulary and, fortunately, not understood if they were ever heard. The supreme value of horse breeding was that it always gave both the horseman and his master something to look forward to. They could look forward to the arrival of the foal, they could watch with pleasure the development of the colts, the pleasure of breaking them in and teaching them work, and if one could breed an animal and show it, and win a competition with others, it would produce a curious feeling of one-upmanship to all those concerned.

Ben had plenty of good horses as he regularly bred them. The time factor was unimportant as he and his horseman were always fully occupied while their development took place. At one time he had twelve of Kitty's descendants either working or running about as colts on his farms.

"Young men afraid of old horses", ruminated Old Thomas's grandson.

Since that was genuinely the case, Ben had perforce to accept it. The horses went and another combine came.

Epilogue

In the foreword of Frank Smith's 1893 account book is the following paragraph:

> It is suggested that the British Agriculturalist must entirely alter his course of cultivation, and that he must call in the aid of science and apply himself with more zeal and ability to every detail of his business. It may be reasonably hoped that the rising generation of farmers and farm workers will be better educated than the present race, and that they receive instruction in those rudiments of technical education and scientific agriculture which were almost unknown to their fathers.

Fulfilment of these prophetic hopes have seen the art of agriculture submerged by science. The Corn Exchange, with the farm horse, half the farmers and three quarters of the farm workers have passed into history.

***